1001 more QUESTIONS on the BIBLE

LARRY PIATT

BAKER BOOK HOUSE
Grand Rapids, Michigan 49506

This book is dedicated
to my wonderful wife,
Lynn,
and my three lovely daughters:
Stephanie, Jennifer, and Catherine.

Copyright © 1986 by Baker Books
a division of Baker Book House Company
P.O. Box 6287, Grand Rapids, MI 49516-6287

ISBN: 0-8010-7094-5

Eighth printing, June 1996

All Scripture quotations are from the King James Version.

Printed in the United States of America

Sample: Who was Adam's wife?
A. Elisabeth   B. Eve   C. Sarah   D. Ruth

1. On which day did God say, "Let there be light"?
A. First   B. Second   C. Fourth   D. Sixth

2. What did God create on the second day?
A. Fish   B. Trees   C. Fowl   D. Firmament

3. What did God call the dry land?
A. Earth   B. Dust   C. Eden   D. Ground

4. What did God call the waters which were gathered together?
A. Oceans   B. Rivers   C. Seas   D. Lakes

5. What did God create on the third day?
A. Sun, moon, and stars   B. Trees and grass   C. Man   D. Fish

6. What did God create on the fourth day?
A. Fowl   B. Fish   C. Sun, moon, and stars   D. Trees and grass

7. What did God create on the fifth day?
A. Man   B. Cattle   C. Stars   D. Fish and fowl

8. What did God create on the sixth day?
A. Cattle   B. Fish and fowl   C. Trees and grass   D. Seas

9. On which day was man created?
A. Fourth   B. Fifth   C. Sixth   D. Seventh

10. On which day did God rest?
A. Sixth   B. Seventh   C. Eighth   D. Tenth

11. God breathed into Adam "and man became a living _____."
A. Creature   B. Soul   C. Being   D. Son

12. "And the LORD God planted a garden eastward in _____."
A. Egypt   B. Israel   C. Gethsemane   D. Eden

13. Adam was commanded not to eat the fruit from which tree?
A. Tree of the knowledge of good and evil   B. Apple tree
C. Orange tree   D. Tree of Life

14. Who named all the animals?
A. Adam   B. Eve   C. God   D. Cain

15. What did God take from Adam?
A. His wife   B. His sons   C. His rib   D. His breath

16. What did God make from Adam's rib?
    A. Woman   B. Children   C. Dinner   D. Abel

17. Who "was more subtil than any beast of the field"?
    A. Adam   B. God   C. Eve   D. The serpent

18. Whom did the serpent tempt?
    A. God   B. Eden   C. Eve   D. Adam

19. Who said, "Ye shall not surely die"?
    A. God   B. The serpent   C. Adam   D. Eve

20. Who clothed Adam and Eve with fig leaves?
    A. The serpent   B. God   C. They clothed themselves   D. Abel

21. Who called to Adam, "Where art thou?"
    A. Eve   B. God   C. The serpent   D. Cain and Abel

22. To whom did God say, "Upon thy belly shalt thou go"?
    A. Adam   B. Eve   C. Satan   D. The serpent

23. To whom did God say, "In sorrow thou shalt bring forth children"?
    A. Eve   B. The serpent   C. Eden   D. Sarah

24. To whom did God say, "Cursed is the ground for thy sake"?
    A. Adam   B. Eve   C. The serpent   D. Lucifer

25. God said Adam would return unto what?
    A. Eve   B. Dust   C. Eden   D. God

26. Why did God cast Adam out of the Garden of Eden?
    A. As punishment for disobedience   B. God hated him
    C. So he wouldn't eat from the tree of knowledge
    D. So he wouldn't eat from the tree of life

27. Who was Adam's first son?
    A. Abel   B. Seth   C. Cain   D. Judah

28. Who was Adam's second son?
    A. Abel   B. Seth   C. Cain   D. Judah

29. What was Abel's occupation?
    A. Craftsman   B. Carpenter   C. Farmer   D. Shepherd

30. What was Cain's occupation?
    A. Craftsman   B. Carpenter   C. Farmer   D. Shepherd

31. Whose offering did God accept?
    A. Cain's   B. Abel's   C. Adam's   D. Eve's

32. Whose offering did God reject?

    A. Cain's B. Abel's C. Adam's D. Eve's

33. To whom did God say, "The voice of thy brother's blood crieth unto me from the ground"?

    A. Adam B. Cain C. Seth D. Abel

34. God said that if anyone killed Cain, vengeance would "be taken on him _____."

    A. Twofold B. Fourfold C. Sevenfold D. Tenfold

35. Cain dwelt east of Eden in the land of _____.

    A. Syria B. Egypt C. Barrenness D. Nod

36. Who was Cain's son?

    A. Israel B. Seth C. Lamech D. Enoch

37. Seth was whose son?

    A. Lamech's B. Noah's C. Abel's D. Adam's

38. How old was Adam when he died?

    A. 120 B. 88 C. 707 D. 930

39. Who was the second oldest man in the Bible?

    A. Adam B. Jared C. Enoch D. Noah

40. Who was Enoch's son?

    A. Methuselah B. Noah C. Jared D. Shem

41. Who lived to be 969 years old?

    A. Methuselah B. Noah C. Jared D. Enoch

42. Who was Noah's father?

    A. Terah B. Lamech C. Methuselah D. Enoch

43. From what kind of wood did Noah build the ark?

    A. Oak B. Gopher C. Hyssop D. Walnut

44. How long was the ark?

    A. 50 cubits (75 feet) B. 300 cubits (450 feet)
    C. 400 cubits (600 feet) D. 30 cubits (45 feet)

45. How wide was the ark?

    A. 50 cubits (75 feet) B. 300 cubits (450 feet)
    C. 400 cubits (600 feet) D. 30 cubits (45 feet)

46. How high was the ark?

    A. 50 cubits (75 feet) B. 300 cubits (450 feet)
    C. 400 cubits (600 feet) D. 30 cubits (45 feet)

47. How many stories did the ark have?
   A. 1   B. 2   C. 3   D. 4

48. Noah took how many of each clean animal?
   A. 2   B. 4   C. 7   D. 12

49. Noah took how many of each unclean animal?
   A. 2   B. 4   C. 7   D. 12

50. How old was Noah at the time of the flood?
   A. 150   B. 300   C. 500   D. 600

51. How long was the flood water on the earth?
   A. 40 days   B. 90 days   C. 150 days   D. 300 days

52. How long was Noah's family in the ark?
   A. 3 months   B. 6 months   C. 1 year   D. Over 1 year

53. Who was Canaan's father?
   A. Shem   B. Ham   C. Japheth   D. Noah

54. Who found Noah drunk in his tent?
   A. Shem   B. Ham   C. Japheth   D. Canaan

55. When Noah awoke, whom did he curse?
   A. Shem   B. Ham   C. Japheth   D. Canaan

56. How old was Noah when he died?
   A. 120   B. 335   C. 752   D. 950

57. Who was called "the mighty hunter before the Lord"?
   A. Babel   B. Esau   C. Nimrod   D. Elijah

58. Who was Abraham's father?
   A. Terah   B. Lot   C. Isaac   D. Shem

59. Who was Lot's father?
   A. Terah   B. Haran   C. Nahor   D. Abraham

60. From what city was Abraham?
   A. Ur   B. Babylon   C. Nineveh   D. Susa

61. To what country did Abraham go to escape a famine?
   A. Canaan   B. Syria   C. Egypt   D. Philistia

62. In Egypt, Abraham feared for his life because of his _____.
   A. Fame   B. Herds   C. Riches   D. Wife

63. Whose house was plagued because he had taken Sarah?
   A. Lot's   B. Pharaoh's   C. Abraham's   D. Laban's

64. After Lot and Abraham separated, where did Lot go?
    A. Egypt   B. The mountains of Edom   C. Tyre
    D. Towards Sodom

65. Who was the "king of Salem" and "the priest of the most high God"?
    A. Aaron   B. Abraham   C. Melchizedek   D. Levi

66. Who was Abraham's steward?
    A. Eliezer   B. Lot   C. Sarah   D. Isaac

67. While Abraham was in a deep sleep, God told him that his descendants would be slaves in Egypt for how long?
    A. 40 years   B. 70 years   C. 210 years   D. 400 years

68. Hagar was whose handmaid?
    A. Abraham's   B. Sarah's   C. Isaac's   D. Ruth's

69. What nationality was Hagar?
    A. Egyptian   B. Syrian   C. Ethiopian   D. Israelite

70. Sarah dealt harshly with whom?
    A. Abraham   B. Hagar   C. Ishmael   D. Isaac

71. Who found Hagar in the wilderness?
    A. Abraham   B. Sarah   C. Ishmael   D. An angel

72. Ishmael was the son of Hagar and whom?
    A. Isaac   B. Jacob   C. Esau   D. Abraham

73. How old was Abraham when Ishmael was born?
    A. 25   B. 56   C. 86   D. 100

74. What was Abraham's former name?
    A. Abram   B. Aaron   C. Adam   D. Abijah

75. Whose name meant "father of many nations"?
    A. Adam's   B. Jehovah's   C. Abraham's   D. Isaac's

76. What land did God give to Abraham?
    A. Egypt   B. Canaan   C. Syria   D. Jerusalem

77. What was Sarah's former name?
    A. Serug   B. Nahor   C. Salem   D. Sarai

78. Who did Abraham want as his heir?
    A. Eliezer   B. Laban   C. Ishmael   D. Sarah

79. When Sarah heard the Lord tell Abraham that she would have a son, what did Sarah do?
    A. Hid   B. Ran into the desert   C. Worshiped God   D. Laughed

80. As the Lord spoke with Abraham, two angels went toward _____.

    A. Sodom   B. Jerusalem   C. Heaven   D. Jericho

81. Abraham asked the Lord to spare Sodom if that city had how many righteous men?

    A. 50   B. 60   C. 70   D. 80

82. The Lord agreed. Then Abraham asked the Lord to spare Sodom if there were how many righteous men?

    A. 75   B. 65   C. 55   D. 45

83. After the Lord agreed, Abraham asked that Sodom be spared if _____ righteous men were there.

    A. 60   B. 50   C. 40   D. 35

84. Abraham next pleaded to spare Sodom for _____ righteous men.

    A. 35   B. 33   C. 31   D. 30

85. The Lord next agreed not to destroy Sodom "for _____ sake."
    A. Thirty-five's   B. Twenty-five's   C. Twenty's   D. Fifteen's

86. Abraham asked and the Lord agreed not to destroy Sodom if there were _____ righteous men.

    A. 15   B. 10   C. 5   D. Any

87. How many angels arrived at Sodom?
    A. 1   B. 2   C. 3   D. 4

88. Who invited the angels to stay the night?
    A. The men of Sodom   B. Abraham   C. Isaac   D. Lot

89. Who wanted to see the angels?
    A. Lot's daughters   B. The men of Sodom   C. Lot's wife
    D. Ishmael

90. Who was struck with blindness?
    A. The men of Sodom   B. Lot's wife   C. Lot   D. The angels

91. Who ignored Lot's warning to flee from Sodom?
    A. His daughters   B. His sons-in-law   C. His wife   D. The angels

92. How many daughters did Lot have?
    A. None   B. 2   C. 3   D. 4

93. To what city did Lot and his family flee?
    A. Sodom   B. Gomorrah   C. Zoar   D. Jericho

94. Lot had two sons, Moab and Ben-Ammi. Who were their mothers?
    A. Lot's wife   B. Sarah   C. Lot's daughters   D. Esther

95. Moab was the father of the Moabites. Ben-Ammi was the father of the
    _____.
    A. Benjamites   B. Ammonites   C. Edomites   D. Hittites

96. Who took Sarah after Abraham said, "She is my sister"?
    A. Abimelech   B. Lot   C. Laban   D. Isaac

97. Abraham explained that he and Sarah had the same _____.
    A. Father   B. Mother   C. Sisters   D. Brothers

98. Who showed Hagar the well of water in the wilderness?
    A. An angel   B. Abraham   C. God   D. Sarah

99. Who made a covenant with Abraham?
    A. Sarah   B. Abimelech   C. Ishmael   D. Isaac

100. Where was this covenant made?
     A. Beer-sheba   B. Jerusalem   C. Jericho   D. Cana

101. Who was Phichol?
     A. Abraham's servant.   B. King of the Philistines
     C. Abimelech's captain   D. Hagar's son

102. Who said, "My son, God will provide himself a lamb for a burnt offering"?
     A. God   B. Abraham   C. Isaac   D. Esau

103. In what did Abraham bury Sarah?
     A. A grave   B. A tomb   C. A casket   D. A cave

104. It was called the cave of the field of _____.
     A. Machpelah   B. Abraham   C. Jerusalem   D. Death

105. From whom did Abraham buy the cave?
     A. Isaac   B. Ephron   C. Lot   D. Laban

106. Whom did Abraham send to get a wife for Isaac?
     A. Isaac   B. Himself   C. A servant   D. Lot

107. Who gave water to Abraham's servant and his animals?
     A. Rachel   B. Rebekah   C. Leah   D. Dinah

108. Who was Rebekah's father?
     A. Bethuel   B. Laban   C. Lot   D. Levi

109. Who was Rebekah's brother?
     A. Bethuel   B. Laban   C. Lot   D. Levi

110. What relation were Isaac and Rebekah?

A. Cousins   B. Uncle and niece   C. Aunt and nephew
D. No relation

111. Who was Abraham's second wife?

A. Hagar   B. Leah   C. Keturah   D. Deborah

112. Where was Abraham buried?

A. Jerusalem   B. Egypt   C. Shiloh   D. The cave of Machpelah

113. Who buried Abraham?

A. God   B. Isaac   C. Ishmael   D. Isaac and Ishmael

114. How old was Isaac when he married Rebekah?

A. 20   B. 30   C. 40   D. 50

115. Which of Isaac's sons was born first?

A. Esau   B. Jacob   C. Joseph   D. Reuben

116. How old was Isaac when his sons were born?

A. 30   B. 40   C. 50   D. 60

117. Jacob sold a meal to Esau for what?

A. 20 pieces of silver   B. Esau's birthright   C. 4 Sheep
D. Esau's bow

118. What kind of meat did Isaac ask Esau to bring him?

A. Pork   B. Venison   C. Beef   D. Veal

119. Who helped Jacob deceive Isaac for a blessing?

A. Rebekah   B. Rachel   C. Esau   D. No one

120. What did Esau plan to do after Isaac's death?

A. Get married   B. Leave home   C. Kill Jacob
D. Tend Isaac's herds

121. Esau married a woman who was the daughter of whom?

A. Abraham   B. Lot   C. Ishmael   D. Isaac

122. What did Jacob call the place where God spoke to him?

A. Jericho   B. Jerusalem   C. Shiloh   D. Bethel

123. What relation were Jacob and Rachel?

A. Brother and sister   B. Cousins   C. Aunt and nephew
D. Uncle and niece

124. Who was Laban's older daughter?

A. Leah   B. Rachel   C. Dinah   D. Rebekah

125. Who was Leah's handmaid?
    A. Rachel   B. Bilhah   C. Zilpah   D. Dinah

126. Who was Rachel's handmaid?
    A. Leah   B. Bilhah   C. Zilpah   D. Dinah

127. Who did Jacob love best?
    A. Rachel   B. Leah   C. Esau   D. Laban

128. Who was the mother of Jacob's first son, Reuben?
    A. Rachel   B. Leah   C. Bilhah   D. Zilpah

129. Who was the mother of Simeon, Levi, Judah, Issachar, and Zebulun?
    A. Rachel   B. Leah   C. Bilhah   D. Zilpah

130. Who was the mother of Dan and Naphtali?
    A. Rachel   B. Leah   C. Bilhah   D. Zilpah

131. Who was the mother of Gad and Asher?
    A. Rachel   B. Leah   C. Bilhah   D. Zilpah

132. Who was the mother of Jacob's only daughter, Dinah?
    A. Rachel   B. Leah   C. Bilhah   D. Zilpah

133. Who was the mother of Joseph and Benjamin?
    A. Rachel   B. Leah   C. Bilhah   D. Zilpah

134. Who stole Laban's images (idols)?
    A. Jacob   B. Leah   C. Rachel   D. Reuben

135. How many years did Jacob work for Laban?
    A. 7   B. 14   C. 20   D. 30

136. How many times did Laban change Jacob's wages?
    A. 3   B. 7   C. 10   D. 12

137. Where did Jacob wrestle with the angel?
    A. Peniel   B. Bethel   C. Jerusalem   D. Jericho

138. What part of Jacob's body was hurt after wrestling with the angel?
    A. Eye   B. Knee   C. Arm   D. Thigh

139. Who wanted to marry Dinah, Jacob's daughter?
    A. Esau   B. Shechem   C. Hamor   D. Reuben

140. Who was Shechem's father?
    A. Hamor   B. Esau   C. Lot   D. Ishmael

141. Who killed Shechem and Hamor?
    A. Jacob   B. Esau   C. Simeon and Levi   D. Reuben and Judah

142. When Rachel died after giving birth to Benjamin, Jacob buried her near what town?

A. Bethlehem   B. Jericho   C. Shechem   D. Jerusalem

143. How old was Isaac when he died?

A. 70   B. 80   C. 100   D. 180

144. Who buried Isaac?

A. Jacob   B. Esau   C. Jacob and Esau   D. Ishmael

145. Where was Isaac buried?

A. Egypt   B. The cave of Machpelah   C. Shiloh   D. Jerusalem

146. Esau was the father of the _____.

A. Canaanites   B. Hittites   C. Ammonites   D. Edomites

147. Esau lived where?

A. Mt. Seir   B. Jerusalem   C. Shiloh   D. Jericho

148. What were Esau's descendants called?

A. Princes   B. Dukes   C. Lords   D. Kings

149. Who dreamed about his brother's sheaves bowing to his sheaf?

A. Jacob   B. Esau   C. Joseph   D. Levi

150. Who dreamed of the sun, moon, and eleven stars bowing before him?

A. Esau   B. Reuben   C. Jacob   D. Joseph

151. Who persuaded the brothers to sell Joseph to the Ishmaelites?

A. Reuben   B. Levi   C. Judah   D. The Ishmaelites

152. Who had twin sons by his daughter-in-law, Tamar?

A. Jacob   B. Reuben   C. Joseph   D. Judah

153. Who dreamed of a vine with three branches that produced grapes?

A. Joseph   B. The butler   C. The baker   D. Pharaoh

154. What did this dream mean?

A. The butler would serve Pharaoh   B. Joseph would serve Pharaoh
C. The baker would serve Pharaoh   D. A famine was coming

155. Who dreamed of birds eating food out of a basket he carried?

A. Joseph   B. The butler   C. The baker   D. Pharaoh

156. What did this dream mean?

A. The butler would be hanged   B. The baker would be hanged
C. Joseph would be hanged   D. A famine was coming

157. Who forgot to talk to Pharaoh about Joseph?

A. The butler   B. The baker   C. Potiphar   D. The jailer

158. What was Pharaoh's first dream about?

A. Locusts   B. Corn   C. Hail   D. Cattle

159. What was Pharaoh's second dream about?

A. Locusts   B. Corn   C. Cattle   D. Hail

160. What did the 7 fat cattle and 7 good ears of corn represent?

A. 7 years of plenty   B. 7 years of famine   C. 7 days of sunshine
D. 7 days of pestilence

161. What did the 7 thin cattle and 7 bad ears of corn represent?

A. 7 years of plenty   B. 7 years of famine   C. 7 days of sunshine
D. 7 days of pestilence

162. What did Joseph's brothers find in their grain sacks?

A. Joseph's cup   B. Pebbles   C. Sand   D. Money

163. Who promised Jacob he would protect Benjamin in Egypt?

A. Reuben   B. Simeon   C. Levi   D. Joseph

164. From which of Jacob's sons did Jesus descend?

A. Joseph   B. Reuben   C. Judah   D. Levi

165. Where was Jacob buried?

A. Egypt   B. Jerusalem   C. Jericho   D. The cave of Machpelah

166. Who said, "Ye thought evil against me; but God meant it unto good"?

A. Moses   B. Joseph   C. Jacob   D. Pharaoh

167. In Exodus, who were Shiphrah and Puah?

A. Moses' parents   B. Moses' sisters   C. Hebrew midwives
D. Pharaoh's sons

168. Who wanted to kill Moses?

A. Pharaoh   B. Aaron   C. God   D. Miriam

169. How many daughters did Reuel have?

A. 3   B. 5   C. 7   D. 10

170. Who was called "I AM"?

A. God   B. Moses   C. Pharaoh   D. Aaron

171. What happened when Moses threw his rod on the ground?

A. God punished him   B. The rod turned to blood   C. Nothing
D. The rod became a serpent

172. What happened when Moses touched the serpent's tail?

A. It bit him   B. Nothing   C. It became a rod   D. It vanished

173. What happened to Moses' hand?

A. It had leprosy   B. The snake bit it   C. Moses burned it
D. Moses cut it

174. After Pharaoh refused to let Israel go, he said the Israelites would gather what to make their bricks?

A. Mortar   B. Stones   C. Straw   D. Water

175. God told Moses that Abraham, Isaac, and Jacob didn't know Him by His name _____.

A. Lord   B. Jehovah   C. Elohim   D. Adonai

176. Who were Amram and Jochebed?

A. Pharaoh's magicians   B. Moses' brother and sister
C. Pharaoh's sons   D. Moses' parents

177. After which plague did Pharaoh's magicians say, "This is the finger of God"?

A. Frogs   B. Hail   C. Lice   D. Flies

178. For how many days was the plague of darkness upon Egypt?

A. 3   B. 7   C. 10   D. 21

179. God said, "When I see the _____, I will pass over you."

A. Star   B. Cross   C. Blood   D. Angel

180. How many plagues came upon Egypt?

A. 3   B. 7   C. 10   D. 12

181. When did God kill the firstborn in Egypt?

A. Midnight   B. Noon   C. At the ninth hour   D. At the third hour

182. God said to Moses, "Sanctify unto me all the _____."

A. Males   B. Firstborn   C. Cattle   D. Gold

183. Why did the Israelites complain at Marah?

A. There was no food   B. There was no water
C. The water was bitter   D. Moses was going too fast

184. How was the problem solved?

A. They traveled until they found good water
B. Moses got water out of a rock   C. They dug a well
D. Moses threw a tree in the waters which made them sweet

185. What place had 12 wells and 70 palm trees?

A. Elim   B. Jericho   C. Jerusalem   D. Sinai

186. How many years did the Israelites eat manna?

   A. 7   B. 14   C. 21   D. 40

187. In what year would a Hebrew servant be set free?

   A. First   B. Third   C. Seventh   D. Tenth

188. The Israelites were not to sow anything in their fields in what year?

   A. Second   B. Third   C. Seventh   D. Ninth

189. How many of Israel's elders went up Mt. Sinai with Moses?

   A. None   B. 1   C. 12   D. 70

190. Who was Moses' minister?

   A. Aaron   B. Joshua   C. God   D. Nadab

191. Whom did God choose to make the tabernacle?

   A. Moses and Aaron   B. Bezaleel and Aholiab
   C. Joshua and Caleb   D. Aaron and Hur

192. When Moses asked "Who is on the LORD's side?" the sons of
   _____ responded.

   A. Levi   B. Moses   C. Aaron   D. Judah

193. How many men did the Levites kill?

   A. 30   B. 300   C. 3,000   D. 30,000

194. For how many days did Moses not eat or drink?

   A. 3   B. 7   C. 12   D. 40

195. According to Leviticus, one who stole something had to return what he
   stole plus give how much more?

   A. 1/10   B. 1/5   C. 1/3   D. 1/4

196. What did Moses put on Aaron's right ear, right thumb, and right big toe?

   A. Salve   B. Honey   C. Oil   D. Blood

197. Israel was to celebrate 7 feasts. On the fourteenth day of the first month
   they celebrated what?

   A. Passover   B. Pentecost   C. Firstfruits   D. Tabernacles

198. On the fifteenth day of the first month, Israel celebrated a 7-day feast
   called the Feast of what?

   A. Passover   B. Pentecost   C. Unleavened Bread   D. Trumpets

199. On Sunday during the Feast of Unleavened Bread, Israel held the Feast
   of what?

   A. Trumpets   B. Tabernacles   C. Pentecost   D. Firstfruits

200. Israel celebrated Pentecost which took place _____ days after the Feast of Firstfruits.

A. 30   B. 40   C. 50   D. 60

201. On the first day of the seventh month, Israel celebrated the Feast of what?

A. Pentecost   B. Trumpets   C. Tabernacles   D. Passover

202. On the first day of the seventh month, Israel celebrated the day of what?

A. Atonement   B. Dedication   C. New Year   D. Thanksgiving

203. On the fifteenth day of the seventh month, Israel began a 7-day feast called the Feast of what?

A. Dedication   B. Tabernacles   C. Trumpets   D. Thanksgiving

204. What happened to Shelomith's son, who during a fight, cursed God?

A. He was banished from Israel.   B. He was sent back to Egypt.
C. He was beaten with 40 stripes.   D. He was stoned to death.

205. The fiftieth year was called the year of what?

A. Redemption   B. Jubilee   C. Rejoicing   D. Atonement

206. Numbers explains that for a certain sin, the priest made the accused woman drink bitter water. What was the sin?

A. Adultery   B. Gossip   C. False witness   D. Stealing

207. One who took the Nazarite vow was forbidden to do what?

A. Drink strong drink.   B. Cut his hair.   C. Touch a dead body
D. All of the above.

208. What was indicated when one who had taken the Nazarite vow shaved his head?

A. He was disobeying God's command.   B. His vow had begun.
C. He had completed his vow.   D. The vow was permanent.

209. Which tribe was dedicated to God instead of all the firstborn in Israel?

A. Judah   B. Levi   C. Dan   D. Reuben

210. The Levites served in the tabernacle from age 25 to what?

A. 30   B. 40   C. 50   D. 60

211. Moses called one place Taberah, because God killed some of the people with what?

A. Fire   B. Hailstones   C. Flood   D. Pestilence

212. To help Moses, God poured out His Spirit on _____ elders of Israel.

A. 12   B. 40   C. 56   D. 70

213. Two of these elders, Eldad and Medad, prophesied in the camp. Who wanted Moses to stop them?

A. Aaron   B. Miriam   C. Joshua   D. Hur

214. After God had commanded Israel to wander in the wilderness for 40 years, some tried to go into the Promised Land. What happened to them?

A. God killed them with a pestilence
B. The Amalekites and Canaanites fought them
C. They entered and prospered in the Promised Land
D. Moses banished them from Israel

215. What happened to the man caught gathering sticks on the sabbath?
A. He was banished to Egypt   B. He was killed by lightning
C. He was told to stop   D. He was stoned to death

216. How many princes rebelled with Korah, Dathan, and Abiram?
A. 12   B. 40   C. 120   D. 250

217. These princes were told to put what in their censers?
A. Incense   B. Bread   C. Doves   D. Water

218. What happened to these princes?
A. They were banished to Egypt   B. They were stoned to death
C. God killed them with fire   D. The earth swallowed them

219. What was made from the 250 censers?

A. An idol   B. Brass plates that covered the altar
C. Brass shields for the Levites   D. A brass cauldron

220. What happened to the people who accused Moses and Aaron of killing God's people?

A. They were struck by lightning
B. They were bitten by poisonous snakes
C. They were killed by fire from God
D. They were killed in a plague

221. Whose rod budded, blossomed, and yielded almonds?

A. Moses'   B. Aaron's   C. Joshua's   D. Caleb's

222. Which country did not let Israel pass through its land?

A. Edom   B. Egypt   C. Syria   D. Babylonia

223. Who died in Mt. Hor?

A. Aaron   B. Moses   C. Joshua   D. Miriam

224. For how many days did Israel mourn his death?

A. 3   B. 10   C. 21   D. 30

225. Who was the king of the Canaanites that Israel defeated?

A. Barak   B. Balaam   C. Arad   D. Enoch

226. Who was the king of the Amorites that Israel defeated?

A. Barak   B. Sihon   C. Og   D. Balaam

227. Who was the king of Bashan that Israel defeated?

A. Barak   B. Sihon   C. Og   D. Balaam

228. What physical characteristic did Og have?

A. He had 6 fingers on each hand.   B. He was a giant.
C. He was left-handed.   D. He only had one leg.

229. What did Og have that was 9 cubits long?

A. A chariot   B. A spear.   C. A bed.   D. A leg.

230. A plague killed 24,000 because Israel had worshiped the gods of _____.

A. Egypt   B. Ammon   C. Edom   D. Moab

231. The plague stopped when Zimri and Cozbi were killed by whom?

A. Moses   B. Joshua   C. Phinehas   D. God

232. Whose son was he?

A. Eleazar's   B. Moses'   C. Aaron's   D. Joshua's

233. What did the daughters of Zelophehad want?

A. Husbands   B. An inheritance   C. Vengeance   D. Forgiveness

234. One of Zelophehad's daughters had the same name as a famous man in the Bible. What was her name?

A. Noah   B. Moses   C. Israel   D. Daniel

235. The daughters of Zelophehad had to marry whom?

A. Levites   B. Priests   C. Moabites   D. Men from their own tribe

236. If a person killed another accidentally, he could flee to a city of _____.

A. Safety   B. Vengeance   C. Justice   D. Refuge

237. How many of these cities were there?

A. 3   B. 6   C. 7   D. 12

238. The one who fled to a city of refuge had to stay there until who died?

A. The victim   B. The avenger   C. The high priest   D. The judge

239. In which year of Israel's wanderings is the book of Deuteronomy set?

A. Thirty-fifth   B. Twelfth   C. Fortieth   D. Tenth

240. If a man was to be punished by beating, he could not be beaten with more than _____ stripes.

A. 10   B. 20   C. 30   D. 40

18

241. What people did God command Israel to wipe out?

    A. Amalek   B. Edom   C. Ammon   D. Moab

242. For how many days did Israel mourn Moses' death?

    A. 14   B. 21   C. 30   D. 40

243. In the book following Deuteronomy, to whom did God say, "As I was with Moses, so I will be with thee"?

    A. Aaron   B. Eleazar   C. Joshua   D. Caleb

244. God said Joshua was to meditate upon what?

    A. Moses' life   B. God   C. The book of the law
    D. The Promised Land

245. Reuben, Gad, and half the tribe of _____ inherited land on the east side of the river Jordan.

    A. Manasseh   B. Dan   C. Judah   D. Issachar

246. What did Rahab do with the two spies Joshua had sent?

    A. Gave them to the king of Jericho   B. Hid them
    C. Killed them   D. Imprisoned them

247. Where did she hide them?

    A. In barrels of corn meal   B. In the king's stable
    C. Under the bed   D. On the roof

248. What did Rahab tell the king about the spies?

    A. I don't know what you're talking about
    B. The spies had left Jericho
    C. The spies were hidden
    D. The spies had not come to her house

249. Who saw the captain of the host of the Lord?

    A. Joshua   B. Caleb   C. The two spies   D. All Israel

250. Who was to take off his shoes since he was standing on holy ground?

    A. Eleazar   B. The men of Israel   C. Caleb   D. Joshua

251. Joshua pronounced a curse on the man who built what?

    A. Idols   B. Jericho   C. A temple   D. His own reputation

252. Who took a Babylonian garment, silver, and gold from Jericho?

    A. Joshua   B. Achan   C. Caleb   D. Eleazar

253. Where had Achan hidden this loot?

    A. Under a tree   B. In Jericho   C. In his tent   D. Under a rock

254. What city defeated Israel?

    A. Hebron   B. Bethel   C. Ai   D. Gibeon

255. What happened to Achan and his family?

A. They were stoned to death
B. They were banished from Israel
C. They were sent back to Egypt
D. They were left in the wilderness

256. Who did Israel make "hewers of wood and drawers of water"?

A. The Levites   B. The people of Jericho   C. Joshua's sons
D. The Gibeonites

257. A confederacy of kings was formed by Adoni-zedec, who was king of what city?

A. Jericho   B. Hebron   C. Jerusalem   D. Hazor

258. After Joshua defeated them in battle, where did the 5 kings hide?

A. In barrels of meal   B. In a haystack   C. Under a bridge
D. In a cave

259. How many kings did the Israelites kill while conquering the Promised Land?

A. 7   B. 18   C. 26   D. 31

260. How old was Caleb when Moses sent him to spy out the Promised Land?

A. 30   B. 35   C. 40   D. 50

261. How old was Caleb when he asked Joshua for an inheritance?

A. 60   B. 70   C. 80   D. 85

262. What city did Joshua give to Caleb?

A. Hebron   B. Jerusalem   C. Jericho   D. Bethlehem

263. Whose daughter did Othniel marry?

A. Joshua's   B. Caleb's   C. Moses'   D. Aaron's

264. In what city was the tabernacle set up?

A. Bethlehem   B. Shiloh   C. Jerusalem   D. Hebron

265. How many cities were given to the Levites?

A. 6   B. 0   C. 12   D. 48

266. What did the Reubenites, Gadites, and the half tribe of Manasseh build that infuriated the other tribes?

A. A fenced city   B. An idol   C. an altar   D. A great wall

267. The tribes were angry because they thought the 2½ tribes were _____:

A. Worshiping other gods   B. Making an alliance with Moab
C. Returning to Egypt   D. Making another tabernacle

268. What did they name the altar?

A. Jacob's pride B. Ed C. God's memorial
D. The pledge of freedom

269. Where did Joshua deliver his farewell address?

A. Jerusalem B. Shiloh C. Gaza D. Shechem

270. The Book of Judges informs us that the tribes of Judah and Simeon captured Adoni-bezek and cut off his big toes and his what?

A. Hands B. Feet C. Thumbs D. Little fingers

271. Adoni-bezek said he had done the same thing to how many kings?

A. 30 B. 70 C. 87 D. 100

272. Judah did not drive out the inhabitants of the valley because they had what?

A. Egyptian allies B. Chariots of iron C. More warriors D. Giants

273. Who told the Israelites that the inhabitants of the land would be a snare unto them?

A. Joshua B. An angel C. The Lord D. Phinehas

274. Israel was delivered from the king of Mesopotamia by Caleb's son-in-law, _____.

A. Gideon B. Samson C. Ehud D. Othniel

275. Israel was also persecuted by Eglon, who was the king of what country?

A. Edom B. Syria C. Babylon D. Moab

276. Which left-handed judge killed Eglon?

A. Ehud B. Samson C. Gideon D. Barak

277. Israel was oppressed by Jabin, king of what country?

A. Canaan B. Egypt C. Moab D. Assyria

278. Who was Jabin's captain?

A. Nimrod B. Naaman C. Shimei D. Sisera

279. What prophetess was the wife of Lapidoth?

A. Ruth B. Deborah C. Sarah D. Esther

280. Who sent Barak to fight against Sisera?

A. Joshua B. Gideon C. Deborah D. Samson

281. Barak was from what tribe?

A. Dan B. Naphtali C. Judah D. Manasseh

282. Sisera was killed by whom?

A. Jael B. Barak C. Deborah D. He killed himself

283. After Sisera was defeated, who sang a song of praise unto the Lord?
    A. Deborah   B. Barak   C. Deborah and Barak   D. Jael

284. What country next oppressed Israel?
    A. Syria   B. Philistia   C. Babylon   D. Midian

285. Who called Gideon a "mighty man of valour"?
    A. The Lord   B. An angel   C. Deborah   D. A prophet

286. Gideon was from what tribe?
    A. Simeon   B. Manasseh   C. Judah   D. Issachar

287. What did God tell Gideon to do that night?
    A. To pray all night   B. To spy on the Midianites
    C. To gather an army   D. To tear down Baal's altar

288. Who defended Gideon from the men of the city?
    A. His father   B. The Lord   C. An angel   D. His brothers

289. Who was Gideon's father?
    A. Joash   B. Jehu   C. Joshua   D. Jeremiah

290. What was Gideon's other name?
    A. Jephthah   B. Jerubbaal   C. Baalim   D. Samson

291. Why did God say Gideon's army of 32,000 men was too big?
    A. They far outnumbered the enemy
    B. The battle would be over too quickly
    C. There were too many for a sneak attack
    D. They would think they won because of their own strength

292. God told Gideon to tell his army something and 22,000 men left. What did Gideon say?
    A. 22,000 of you must leave   B. If you are afraid, you may go home
    C. If you are a Levite, you may go home
    D. If you are married, you may go home

293. God reduced Gideon's army by another method. What was it?
    A. He chose only the mightiest fighting men
    B. He chose those who drank water from a dipper
    C. He chose the most righteous
    D. He chose those who lapped up water as they drank

294. After all the reductions, how many men were in Gideon's army?
    A. 10,000   B. 5,000   C. 300   D. 120

295. God told Gideon that if he were still unsure, he and his servant should sneak down to the enemy's camp. Who was Gideon's servant?
    A. Baruch   B. Pharez   C. Reuben   D. Phurah

296. What did Gideon hear from the enemy that encouraged him?

A. The enemy's battle plan   B. The size of the Midianite army
C. A man relating a dream he had   D. A message from God's angel

297. The enemy's dream said that something rolled down the hill and knocked over a tent? What was it?

A. Barley bread   B. A pebble   C. A gold nugget   D. Water

298. His friend said that the dream meant what?

A. The Midianites would return home in peace
B. Gideon would defeat the Midianites
C. The Midianites would defeat Gideon
D. His friend didn't know what the dream meant

299. What three things did Gideon give his men?

A. A sword, lamp, and trumpet   B. A horse, sword, and spear
C. A pitcher, lamp, and trumpet   D. A trumpet, sword, and pitcher

300. On Gideon's cue, his men were to say, "The sword of the Lord, and _____."

A. Of Gideon   B. Praise His name   C. On to victory
D. In the power of His might

301. Who were Oreb and Zeeb?

A. Two of Gideon's generals   B. Two Midianite princes
C. Two of God's angels   D. Gideon's sons

302. As Gideon chased the Midianites, he stopped at Succoth and Penuel and asked for what?

A. More horses   B. More men   C. Their prayers   D. Food

303. Who were Zebah and Zalmunna?

A. Gideon's sons   B. Kings of the Midianites
C. Gideon's generals   D. Angels from God

304. What did Gideon do to the 77 elders of Succoth, since they refused to give his men food?

A. He killed them   B. He made them slaves
C. He tied them up with thorns   D. He sent them to Egypt

305. What did Gideon do to the city of Penuel, since they refused to give his men food?

A. He killed all the people   B. He made them all slaves
C. He tore down its tower   D. He destroyed the city

306. Which of Gideon's sons refused to kill Zebah and Zalmunna?

A. Jether   B. Abimelech   C. Jotham   D. Ahaz

307. How many brothers had Gideon's son Abimelech?
A. 12   B. 8   C. 40   D. 70

308. Abimelech killed all his brothers except _____.
A. Jotham   B. Josiah   C. Jebus   D. Joshua

309. Abimelech was made ruler of what city?
A. Jerusalem   B. Nazareth   C. Shechem   D. Shiloh

310. Jotham's parable compared Abimelech to what?
A. An olive tree   B. A fig tree   C. A vine   D. A bramble

311. Who rebelled against Abimelech's rule?
A. Jephthah   B. Gaal   C. Jotham   D. Samson

312. Abimelech destroyed what city?
A. Shiloh   B. Shechem   C. Jerusalem   D. Hebron

313. Who dropped a millstone on Abimelech's head?
A. Jotham   B. Gaal   C. A woman   D. Hiram

314. Who killed Abimelech?
A. His armorbearer   B. Jotham   C. Gaal   D. He killed himself

315. Who loved Delilah?
A. Samuel   B. Gideon   C. Samson   D. Eli

316. Who was the god of the Philistines?
A. Molech   B. Dagon   C. Chemosh   D. Baal

317. Who said, "Let me die with the Philistines"?
A. David   B. Samuel   C. Eli   D. Samson

318. A man named Micah stole money from whom?
A. God   B. His mother   C. Samuel   D. Samson

319. Micah invited a Levite from Bethlehem to stay with him and be his what?
A. Servant   B. Brother   C. Treasurer   D. Priest

320. What tribe stole Micah's idols and priest?
A. Dan   B. Judah   C. Simeon   D. Levi

321. A Levite's concubine was killed by men from what city?
A. Bethlehem   B. Jerusalem   C. Gibeah   D. Hebron

322. In what tribe was the city of Gibeah?
A. Judah   B. Benjamin   C. Dan   D. Ephraim

323. After the battle with Israel, how many men of Benjamin were left?
A. 60   B. 600   C. 6,000   D. 60,000

324. Four hundred wives for the Benjamites were taken from which city?
A. Shechem B. Beersheba C. Jerusalem D. Jabesh-gilead

325. Other wives for the Benjamites were taken at a dance at which city?
A. Bethlehem B. Jebus C. Shiloh D. Gaza

326. How many years did Naomi stay in Moab, according to the Book of Ruth?
A. 1 B. 3 C. 7 D. 10

327. Who was Ruth's first husband?
A. Mahlon B. Chilion C. Elimelech D. Boaz

328. Who died in Moab?
A. Elimelech B. Mahlon C. Chilion D. All of the above

329. Which of Naomi's daughters-in-law stayed in Moab?
A. Ruth B. Orpah C. Chilion D. Esther

330. Who said, "Whither thou goest, I will go"?
A. Orpah B. Naomi C. Ruth D. Boaz

331. Who was the son of Boaz and Ruth?
A. Samuel B. Boaz, Jr. C. Obed D. Ephraim

332. Who was Obed's son?
A. Jesse B. Samuel C. Eli D. David

333. Who was Jesse's son?
A. Eli B. Samuel C. Saul D. David

334. According to First Samuel, Elkanah's wives were Hannah and _____.
A. Ruth B. Peninnah C. Esther D. Tamar

335. Which of Elkanah's wives was childless?
A. Ruth B. Peninnah C. Tamar D. Hannah

336. Each year Elkanah worshiped at what city?
A. Shiloh B. Jerusalem C. Bethlehem D. Hebron

337. What did Hannah ask of the Lord?
A. To punish Peninnah B. Money C. To have a son
D. To bless Elkanah

338. Who thought Hannah was drunk?
A. Eli B. Elkanah C. Peninnah D. Samuel

339. Samuel was the son of Elkanah and _____.
A. Peninnah B. Hannah C. Ruth D. Tamar

340. Who captured the ark of the covenant during a battle?
    A. Israelites   B. Moabites   C. Philistines   D. Edomites

341. How old was Eli when he died?
    A. 68   B. 77   C. 86   D. 98

342. How many years had Eli judged Israel?
    A. 20   B. 30   C. 40   D. 50

343. When Phinehas's wife heard the news of the deaths of her family, what did she name her newborn son?
    A. Eli   B. Ichabod   C. Phinehas   D. Hoshea

344. What does Ichabod mean?
    A. What has happened?   B. Death has come
    C. All hope is gone   D. The glory is departed

345. The Philistines took the ark of the covenant to what city?
    A. Gaza   B. Ashdod   C. Jerusalem   D. Gath

346. In whose temple did the Philistines put the ark?
    A. Baal's   B. Molech's   C. God's   D. Dagon's

347. When the Philistines looked the next morning, what had happened to Dagon?
    A. Nothing   B. It had fallen   C. It had crumbled
    D. It had turned black

348. The following day Dagon had again fallen. But what else had happened?
    A. The ark was aglow   B. Dagon had become dust
    C. Dagon's head and hands were broken off   D. The ark was gone

349. After the Philistines sent the ark away, to which city in Israel did it go?
    A. Beth-shemesh   B. Bethlehem   C. Shiloh   D. Jerusalem

350. Why did God kill the people of Beth-shemesh?
    A. They kept the ark for themselves   B. They touched the ark
    C. They worshiped idols   D. They had looked into the ark

351. Where was the ark kept for 20 years?
    A. Beth-shemesh   B. Jerusalem   C. Kirjath-jearim   D. Hebron

352. The Israelites put away their idols and worshiped at what city?
    A. Jerusalem   B. Mizpeh   C. Shiloh   D. Kirjath-jearim

353. After God helped Israel defeat the Philistines, Samuel set up a stone, commemorating the victory, and called it what?
    A. Ebenezer   B. Shiloh   C. Bethel   D. Achor

354. Where was Samuel's home?

A. Shiloh   B. Jerusalem   C. Bethlehem   D. Ramah

355. Who were Samuel's sons?

A. Hophni and Phinehas   B. Joel and Abiah
C. Nadab and Abihu   D. Cain and Abel

356. Who said of Israel, "They have rejected me, that I should not reign over them"?

A. Samuel   B. Saul   C. God   D. David

357. What did Israel want so they could be like the neighboring countries?

A. A king   B. Idols   C. Chariots   D. More gold

358. Nahash told the people of Jabesh that unless someone saved them he would do what?

A. Kill them   B. Put out their right eyes   C. Burn their city
D. Cut off their right thumbs

359. Who led Israel in defeating Nahash and the Ammonites?

A. Samuel   B. Eli   C. Kish   D. Saul

360. Samuel called for what to come during wheat harvest?

A. Locusts   B. More workers   C. Thunder and rain   D. Fire

361. What did Saul do wrong at Gilgal?

A. He killed a man   B. He stole gold   C. He worshiped an idol
D. He offered a sacrifice

362. Jonathan and who defeated the Philistines in battle?

A. His armorbearer   B. David   C. Saul   D. Samuel

363. Saul had commanded his army not to do what?

A. Flee   B. Sleep   C. Eat   D. Attack

364. Who ate honey?

A. Saul   B. Jonathan   C. Samuel   D. David

365. What did Saul plan to do to Jonathan for eating the honey?

A. Kill him   B. Imprison him   C. Praise him   D. Beat him

366. Who stopped Saul from killing Jonathan?

A. God   B. David   C. Samuel   D. The people of Israel

367. Samuel told Saul to completely destroy whom?

A. Egyptians   B. Philistines   C. Amalekites   D. Syrians

368. Saul spared the life of _____, king of the Amalekites.

A. Joash   B. Agag   C. Besor   D. David

369. Who killed Agag?

A. Samuel   B. Saul   C. David   D. God

370. Who were Eliab, Abinadab, and Shammah?

A. Samuel's sons   B. David's brothers   C. Saul's sons   D. Priests

371. Who played a harp in order to calm Saul?

A. Samuel   B. An angel   C. Saul's wife   D. David

372. Goliath was over _____ feet tall.

A. 7   B. 8   C. 9   D. 10

373. How many sons did Jesse have?

A. 4   B. 6   C. 8   D. 10

374. For how many days did Goliath challenge the Israelite army?

A. 10   B. 20   C. 30   D. 40

375. Goliath was from what city?

A. Gath   B. Ekron   C. Gaza   D. Ashkelon

376. While David tended sheep he killed a lion and a what?

A. Wolf   B. Bear   C. Coyote   D. Fox

377. What did Saul give to David to fight the giant, which David refused?

A. Armor   B. 30 mighty men   C. Sword   D. Spear

378. David faced Goliath with his sling and how many stones?

A. 1   B. 2   C. 4   D. 5

379. Who cut off Goliath's head?

A. David   B. Saul   C. Samuel   D. No one knows

380. Saul promised David that he would marry Saul's older daughter, whose name was what?

A. Michal   B. Merab   C. Ahinoam   D. Ruth

381. How many Philistines did David kill so that he could marry Saul's daughter?

A. 50   B. 100   C. 200   D. 300

382. Who put a statue in David's bed so Saul's soldiers would think it was David?

A. David   B. Michal   C. Saul   D. Jonathan

383. To whom did David flee after Saul tried to kill him?

A. Jesse   B. Jonathan   C. Ziklag   D. Samuel

384. When Saul and his men tried to capture David, they couldn't because they all _____.

A. Began fighting each other   B. Couldn't find David
C. Began prophesying   D. Were struck blind

385. Who threw a javelin at Jonathan?

A. David   B. Saul   C. His armorbearer   D. Abner

386. Jonathan told a boy, "The arrows are beyond thee." What did that mean to David?

A. Everything was safe   B. David should see Jonathan
C. David should flee   D. It meant nothing to David

387. What unusual thing did David and his men eat at Nob?

A. Shewbread   B. Shrimp   C. Manna   D. Venison

388. What priest gave David this bread?

A. Samuel   B. Ahimelech   C. Eli   D. Nathan

389. At Nob, David also took whose sword?

A. Jonathan's   B. Saul's   C. Samuel's   D. Goliath's

390. How did David escape from Achish, king of Gath?

A. He acted like a mad man   B. He lowered himself over the wall
C. He hid in a cart of straw
D. He jumped from a second story window

391. David asked the king of _____ to care for his father and mother.

A. Ammon   B. Moab   C. Edom   D. Egypt

392. What prophet told David to go to Judah?

A. Samuel   B. Iddo   C. Nathan   D. Gad

393. At Saul's command, Doeg the Edomite killed ____ priests.

A. 25   B. 45   C. 65   D. 85

394. Doeg also killed the people of what city?

A. Nob   B. Jerusalem   C. Bethlehem   D. Shiloh

395. David protected Ahimelech's son, whose name was _____.

A. Jonathan   B. Nathan   C. Abiathar   D. Samuel

396. David escaped from Saul and went to what Philistine city?

A. Gath   B. Ekron   C. Gaza   D. Ashkelon

397. What city did Achish give to David?

A. Gath   B. Gaza   C. Jerusalem   D. Ziklag

398. Who went to see the witch of Endor?

A. David   B. Jonathan   C. Saul   D. Abner

399. What happened when the woman saw Samuel?

A. She asked him who he was   B. She cried out   C. She fainted
D. She fell over dead

400. After Samuel pronounced Saul's doom, who made a meal for Saul?

A. The woman   B. Abner   C. Jonathan   D. Samuel

401. Why couldn't David fight with the Philistines against Israel?

A. He refused to fight   B. He was ill
C. The Philistine princes wouldn't let him   D. Saul wouldn't let him

402. Who had burned Ziklag?

A. Ammonites   B. Philistines   C. Egyptians   D. Amalekites

403. David's men spoke of doing what to David?

A. Stoning him   B. Making him king   C. Delivering him to Saul
D. Banishing him to Egypt

404. David and 600 men went after the Amalekites, but how many became
too tired to continue?

A. 100   B. 200   C. 300   D. 400

405. They found a slave of what nationality?

A. Edomite   B. Egyptian   C. Philistine   D. Amalekite

406. When David and his men spotted the Amalekites, what were they doing?

A. Preparing for battle   B. Traveling south   C. Attacking Hebron
D. Eating, drinking, and dancing

407. What did some of David's men want to keep from the 200 who stayed
behind?

A. Food   B. Their families   C. The spoil (booty)   D. Their cattle

408. What did David decide concerning the 200?

A. They would also share the spoil
B. They were to return home   C. They were killed
D. They received no spoil

409. Who was defeated on Mt. Gilboa?

A. The Philistines   B. David's men   C. Israel   D. Babylon

410. The Philistines killed Jonathan, Abinadab, and Melchishua, who were
whose sons?

A. David's   B. Abner's   C. Samuel's   D. Saul's

411. In Second Samuel, an Amalekite told David of Saul's death. According to the Amalekite, who killed Saul?

A. He killed himself B. The Amalekite C. The Philistines
D. Jonathan

412. What happened to the Amalekite?

A. David rewarded him B. David had him killed
C. David banished him from Judah
D. He became king of the Amalekites

413. When Judah made David king, from what city did he reign?

A. Jerusalem B. Ziklag C. Bethlehem D. Hebron

414. How many years did David reign in Hebron?

A. 3½ B. 5 C. 7½ D. 40

415. What did David do when he learned that the men of Jabesh-Gilead had buried Saul?

A. He blessed them B. He killed all the males of Jabesh-Gilead
C. He gave each man 100 pieces of silver D. He cursed them

416. Who made Ish-bosheth king of Israel?

A. God B. Abner C. David D. Saul

417. Who was Ish-bosheth's father?

A. David B. Samuel C. Abner D. Saul

418. How many years did Ish-bosheth rule Israel?

A. 2 B. 5 C. 10 D. 40

419. Joab, David's captain, had two brothers. Who were they?

A. Joel and Abiah B. Abner and Ish-bosheth
C. Abishai and Asahel D. Dan and Beersheba

420. Who chased Abner and was killed by him?

A. Asahel B. Abishai C. Joab D. David

421. Where was Asahel buried?

A. Jerusalem B. Bethlehem C. Hebron D. Dan

422. Ish-bosheth angered Abner by asking about Rizpah, who was _____.

A. Abner's wife B. Ish-bosheth's wife C. Abner's sister
D. Saul's concubine

423. Who offered to ally with David and turn over the kingdom of Israel?

A. Ish-bosheth B. Saul C. Abner D. Joab

424. Who did David want Abner to bring with him when they met?

A. Ish-bosheth B. Michal C. Joab D. His army

31

425. Who killed Abner?

A. Joab   B. David   C. Ish-bosheth   D. Abner

426. In what city was Abner buried?

A. Hebron   B. Jerusalem   C. Samaria   D. Shiloh

427. Who was Jonathan's son?

A. Nadab   B. Michal   C. Joel   D. Mephibosheth

428. How did Mephibosheth become lame?

A. He was injured in war   B. His nurse dropped him
C. He fell from a horse   D. He fell into a well

429. Whom did Rechab and Baanah kill?

A. Joab   B. David   C. Ish-bosheth   D. Mephibosheth

430. Whom did Rechab and Baanah tell of their deed?

A. Joab   B. David   C. Mephibosheth   D. Nathan

431. What did David do to them?

A. He rewarded them   B. He had them killed
C. He blessed them   D. He sent them home

432. In whose tomb was Ish-bosheth's head buried?

A. Abner's   B. David's   C. Samuel's   D. Saul's

433. David attacked Jebus, which is also called what?

A. Samaria   B. Jericho   C. Jerusalem   D. Gaza

434. Which of David's men led the fight to take Jerusalem?

A. Joab   B. Jonathan   C. Abner   D. Abishai

435. When David became king of Israel, for how many years did he reign in Jerusalem?

A. 7   B. 21   C. 33   D. 40

436. As a sign for David to attack the Philistines, God said there would be a sound in what trees?

A. Mulberry   B. Oak   C. Sycamore   D. Cedar

437. What did David take from Abinadab's house?

A. Horses   B. Chariots   C. Sheep   D. The ark of the covenant

438. Who was killed because he touched the ark?

A. Ahio   B. Uzzah   C. Abinadab   D. Joab

439. After Uzzah's death, in whose house did David store the ark?

A. Abinadab's   B. David's   C. Obed-edom's   D. Joab's

440. How long was the ark there?

A. One month   B. Three months   C. Seven months   D. One year

441. God said that David couldn't build a temple but that who would?

A. David's son   B. Nathan   C. Joab   D. The Lord

442. Whose servant was Ziba?

A. David's   B. Joab's   C. Saul's   D. Samuel's

443. Which of Jonathan's sons did David reward?

A. Lo-ammi   B. Zechariah   C. Abner   D. Mephibosheth

444. What was his reward?

A. A talent of gold   B. Twenty golden shields
C. To eat at David's table   D. One hundred Arabian horses

445. Who was to farm Mephibosheth's land?

A. Mephibosheth   B. Ziba   C. David   D. Nathan

446. David sent messengers to comfort Hanun, king of the _____.

A. Ammonites   B. Amorites   C. Edomites   D. Moabites

447. What did Hanun do to David's messengers?

A. He treated them to a banquet   B. He had them killed
C. Imprisoned them   D. He shaved off half their beards

448. When the Ammonites knew that Israel would fight them, who did they hire to help them?

A. Babylonians   B. Egyptians   C. Edomites   D. Syrians

449. Joab led half of Israel's army and who led the other half?

A. David   B. Abishai   C. Abner   D. Nathan

450. Who delivered David's letter to Joab instructing Joab to have Uriah killed?

A. David   B. Abishai   C. Uriah   D. Nathan

451. After Uriah was killed, David married Uriah's wife, whose name was _____.

A. Bathsheba   B. Abigail   C. Dinah   D. Esther

452. In Nathan's parable to David the rich man had killed the poor man's what?

A. Wife   B. Lamb   C. Son   D. Ram

453. What did David say would happen to the rich man?

A. He would pay the poor man twenty pieces of silver
B. He would die   C. He would be banished to Egypt
D. He would pay the poor man ten lambs

454. Who said, "Thou art the man"?
    A. David   B. God   C. Bathsheba   D. Nathan

455. Nathan told David that who would die?
    A. Nathan   B. David   C. David's son   D. Bathsheba

456. Who was Solomon's mother?
    A. Abigail   B. Michal   C. Ahinoam   D. Bathsheba

457. Who was Absalom's sister?
    A. Esther   B. Tamar   C. Dinah   D. Tirzah

458. Who raped Tamar?
    A. Absalom   B. Abner   C. Amnon   D. Asa

459. Who ordered Amnon to be killed?
    A. Absalom   B. David   C. Tamar   D. Nathan

460. Who persuaded a woman of Tekoah to speak to David to allow Absalom
    to come back home?
    A. Joab   B. Absalom   C. Bathsheba   D. Tamar

461. Who did David send to escort Absalom home?
    A. Solomon   B. Tamar   C. Joab   D. Nathan

462. To what city did Joab bring Absalom?
    A. Samaria   B. Bethlehem   C. Damascus   D. Jerusalem

463. Absalom was forbidden to see whom?
    A. Tamar   B. David   C. Solomon   D. Bathsheba

464. After Absalom sent for Joab and Joab didn't come, what did Absalom do?
    A. He sent for Solomon   B. He sent for Joab's wife
    C. He had Joab's field set on fire   D. He sent for Nathan

465. Who persuaded David to let Absalom see him?
    A. Bathsheba   B. Tamar   C. Nathan   D. Joab

466. Which two priests, who were loyal to David, stayed in Jerusalem during
    Absalom's conspiracy?
    A. Joab and Hushai   B. Zadok and Abiathar   C. Ittai and Gad
    D. Ham and Shem

467. What did David tell the priests to carry back to Jerusalem?
    A. The ark of the covenant   B. The table of shewbread
    C. The brass serpent   D. The tabernacle

468. Ziba, Mephibosheth's servant, told David that Mephibosheth was where?

A. At home, waiting for David   B. Fleeing to Edom
C. In Jerusalem, welcoming the new king   D. Buried in Saul's tomb

469. Who wanted to kill Shimei for cursing David?

A. Joab   B. David   C. Nathan   D. Abishai

470. Who advised Absalom to quickly pursue David?

A. Joab   B. Ahithophel   C. Hushai   D. Solomon

471. Who hanged himself when his advice wasn't taken?

A. Ahithophel   B. Joab   C. Solomon   D. Hushai

472. Hushai told the priests Absalom's plans, and the priests told their sons, whose names were what?

A. Joel and Abiah   B. Eleazar and Phineas
C. Ahimaaz and Jonathan   D. Dan and Zophar

473. When Absalom's men chased them, Ahimaaz and Jonathan hid where?

A. In a cave   B. In a tall sycomore tree   C. In a cart of straw
D. In a well

474. Who was Absalom's captain?

A. Joab   B. Amasa   C. Abishai   D. Solomon

475. What relation was Amasa to Joab?

A. His brother   B. His son   C. His nephew   D. His cousin

476. David sent his army out under three captains, whose names were what?

A. Joab, Nathan, and Gad   B. Abishai, Ittai, and Solomon
C. Joab, Abishai, and Ittai   D. David, Solomon, and Joab

477. Whose hair got caught in a tree?

A. Joab's   B. Absalom's   C. Amasa's   D. Abishai's

478. Who wanted to run and give news to David?

A. Jonathan   B. Ahimaaz   C. Hushai   D. Joab

479. But whom did Joab send?

A. Cushi   B. Hushai   C. Ahimaaz   D. Jonathan

480. Who outran Cushi and first came to David?

A. Ahimaaz   B. Joab   C. Hushai   D. Nathan

481. Who told David he must speak to the people instead of mourning for Absalom?

A. Nathan   B. Bathsheba   C. Solomon   D. Joab

482. Who did David say would be the captain of his army?

A. Joab   B. Solomon   C. Amasa   D. Abishai

483. As David returned to Jerusalem, Shimei met him and apologized, but who wanted to kill Shimei?

A. David   B. Solomon   C. Joab   D. Abishai

484. Who said that his servant lied to David about him?

A. Joab   B. Hushai   C. Mephibosheth   D. Nathan

485. The Lord told David that Israel's famine was due to Saul killing the people of what city?

A. Jerusalem   B. Gibeon   C. Gaza   D. Jericho

486. What did the Gibeonites want as payment for Saul's attempt to destroy them?

A. Horses   B. Gold   C. Silver   D. Saul's sons

487. How many of Saul's sons did the Gibeonites kill?

A. 3   B. 5   C. 7   D. 12

488. Who protected the bodies of Saul's sons from the birds and animals?

A. David   B. Solomon   C. The Gibeonites   D. Rizpah

489. David took Saul's bones from Jabesh-Gilead and buried them where?

A. Benjamin   B. Jerusalem   C. Mt. Gilboa   D. Gibeon

490. Who saved David's life when one of Goliath's sons was about to kill David?

A. Joab   B. Abishai   C. Abner   D. Amasa

491. Who was called "the sweet psalmist of Israel"?

A. Solomon   B. Samuel   C. David   D. Nathan

492. When David was thirsty, three of his mighty men got him water from the well in what town?

A. Jerusalem   B. Bethlehem   C. Jericho   D. Gaza

493. What did David do with the water?

A. He drank it   B. He let the men drink it   C. He gave it to a thirsty friend   D. He poured it out

494. Which priest, according to First Kings, followed Adonijah when he tried to rule David's kingdom?

A. Abiathar   B. Zadok   C. Samuel   D. Iddo

495. Which of David's men followed Adonijah?

A. Abishai   B. Nathan   C. Joab   D. Zadok

496. David gave instructions that Solomon should ride David's what?
A. Chariot   B. Horse   C. Camel   D. Mule

497. Who anointed Solomon as king?
A. Abiathar   B. Zadok   C. David   D. Joab

498. Where did God appear to Solomon in a dream?
A. Jerusalem   B. Gibeon   C. Bethlehem   D. Shiloh

499. Who was the man from Tyre who worked in brass?
A. Hiram   B. Jonathan   C. Solomon   D. Nathan

500. Jachin and Boaz refers to two _____.
A. Bodyguards   B. Conquered kings   C. Pillars
D. Of Solomon's sons

501. What did Solomon give Hiram that displeased him?
A. Egyptian horses   B. Syria   C. His daughter   D. Cities

502. Solomon answered all the questions asked him by the queen of
_____.

A. The north   B. Sheba   C. Egypt   D. Heaven

503. Solomon had a throne made of what?
A. Ivory   B. Marble   C. Silver   D. Rubies

504. How many wives did Solomon have?
A. 5   B. 55   C. 300   D. 700

505. How many concubines did Solomon have?
A. 30   B. 73   C. 300   D. 700

506. A prophet told whom that God would give him ten of the tribes of Israel?
A. Rehoboam   B. Solomon   C. Nathan   D. Jeroboam

507. Who was the prophet that told Jeroboam that?
A. Elijah   B. Ahijah   C. Elisha   D. Nathan

508. What did Ahijah tear into twelve pieces to illustrate God's message to Jeroboam?
A. A new garment   B. Solomon's decree   C. A lily of the field
D. His staff

509. Solomon tried to kill Jeroboam, but Jeroboam fled to what country?
A. Syria   B. Babylon   C. Egypt   D. Assyria

510. How many years did Solomon reign?
A. 25   B. 37   C. 40   D. 48

511. When the people asked Rehoboam to treat them kinder than his father Solomon did, who counseled Rehoboam to be a servant to the people?

A. His wife   B. The young counselors   C. Nathan
D. The old counselors

512. Who counseled Rehoboam to make the people's burdens heavier?

A. His wife   B. The young counselors   C. Nathan
D. The old counselors

513. Whose advice did Rehoboam take?

A. His wife   B. The young counselors   C. Nathan
D. The old counselors

514. After Israel rebelled against Rehoboam, who did they stone to death?

A. A tax collector   B. Rehoboam   C. Jeroboam   D. Nathan

515. As Rehoboam prepared to fight the northern tribes, what message did God give through Shemaiah the prophet?

A. God will fight for you   B. Divide the land
C. Kill Jeroboam only   D. Don't fight

516. Who set up golden calves in Dan and Bethel?

A. Rehoboam   B. Joash   C. Jeroboam   D. Amon

517. A man of God prophesied that _____ would burn men's bones on a pagan altar.

A. Jeroboam   B. Rehoboam   C. Hezekiah   D. Josiah

518. Whose hand withered when he tried to capture the man of God?

A. Jeroboam's   B. Rehoboam's   C. Hezekiah's   D. Josiah's

519. What sign was fulfilled to confirm the prophecy of the man of God?

A. Jeroboam became a leper   B. The altar was broken
C. The Egyptians attacked   D. Hail fell

520. Who prayed for Jeroboam's hand to be restored?

A. Elijah   B. Elisha   C. The man of God   D. Jeroboam

521. God said that the man of God would die because he disobeyed God by doing what?

A. Staying in Bethel   B. Accepting money
C. Eating and drinking   D. Killing a goat

522. What killed the man of God?

A. A bear   B. Hail   C. Lightning   D. A lion

523. What was the name of Jeroboam's son who became sick?

A. Abijah   B. Joash   C. Ahijah   D. Eli

524. Jeroboam told his wife to go see which prophet?

A. Elijah   B. Elisha   C. Ahijah   D. Abijah

525. Ahijah told Jeroboam's wife that as soon as she entered the city someone would die. Who?

A. She would   B. Jeroboam   C. Ahijah   D. Abijah

526. During Rehoboam's reign, Judah was attacked by Shishak, king of what country?

A. Syria   B. Egypt   C. Edom   D. Assyria

527. Shishak took away the gold shields, but Rehoboam replaced them with what kind of shields?

A. Silver   B. Brass   C. Iron   D. Gold

528. Why did Asa remove his mother from being queen?

A. She had killed his brother   B. She was a foreigner
C. She had made an idol   D. She had tried to kill him

529. Which prophet met Asa after his defeat of the Ethiopians?

A. Jeremiah   B. Azariah   C. Isaiah   D. Daniel

530. Who did Asa hire to fight Israel?

A. Syria   B. Assyria   C. Babylon   D. Egypt

531. Which prophet rebuked Asa for hiring Syria?

A. Azariah   B. Hosea   C. Nahum   D. Hanani

532. What did Asa do with Hanani?

A. He had him killed   B. He promoted him to chief prophet
C. He sent him away   D. He imprisoned him

533. Asa got a disease in which part of his body?

A. Head   B. Feet   C. Hands   D. Legs

534. Who ruled Israel after Omri?

A. Elijah   B. Ahab   C. Asa   D. Nadab

535. Elijah met one of Ahab's servants whose name was the same as which minor prophet?

A. Micah   B. Jonah   C. Obadiah   D. Joel

536. What had Obadiah done with the Lord's prophets?

A. He hid them from Jezebel   B. He imprisoned them
C. He had them killed   D. He worshiped them

537. On Mount Carmel, how many stones did Elijah use to build an altar?

A. 6   B. 8   C. 10   D. 12

538. How many barrels of water were poured over Elijah's sacrifice?
A. 4   B. 7   C. 8   D. 12

539. Who was the king of Syria who fought Ahab and Israel?
A. Shishak   B. Ben-hadad   C. Cyrus   D. Nebuchadnezzar

540. What did a prophet tell Ahab about fighting Syria?
A. Syria would defeat Israel   B. Surrender to Syria
C. Israel would defeat Syria   D. There would be no war

541. What did the prophet tell Ahab after Israel defeated Syria?
A. Prepare for another battle   B. The Lord has fought for you
C. Syria will win the next battle   D. Repent and follow God

542. Who won the second battle between Israel and Syria?
A. Syria   B. Israel   C. Neither   D. Assyria defeated both of them

543. One of the sons of the prophets told his neighbor to do what?
A. Hit him   B. Move   C. Fight the Syrians   D. Flee to Judah

544. When the man refused to hit the prophet, what happened to him?
A. God rewarded him   B. The prophet hit him
C. A lion killed him   D. Nothing

545. The prophet condemned Ahab for sparing whose life?
A. Jezebel's   B. The prophet's   C. Elijah's   D. Ben-hadad's

546. What did Naboth have that Ahab wanted?
A. A wife   B. A vineyard   C. A horse   D. A house

547. Of what crime was Naboth accused?
A. Blasphemy   B. Murder   C. Adultery   D. Theft

548. What happened to Naboth?
A. He was hanged   B. He was acquitted   C. Nothing
D. He was stoned to death

549. Who met Ahab in Naboth's vineyard?
A. Jezebel   B. Elijah   C. Elisha   D. Iddo

550. What king did Ahab ask to assist him in fighting Syria?
A. Jehu   B. Azariah   C. Jehoshaphat   D. Ahaz

551. What prophet was thrown in prison for telling Ahab he would be killed in battle?
A. Elijah   B. Elisha   C. Nathan   D. Micaiah

552. Who disguised himself during the battle with Syria?
A. Ahab   B. Jehoshaphat   C. Elijah   D. Micaiah

553. Who scolded Jehoshaphat for helping Ahab?

A. Jehu   B. His wife   C. Elijah   D. An angel

554. Where was Ahab buried?

A. Jerusalem   B. Shiloh   C. Samaria   D. Bethel

555. Which king of Israel fell through a lattice?

A. Ahab   B. Jehu   C. Ahaziah   D. Jehoshaphat

556. Ahaziah sent messengers to inquire of Baal-zebub, god of _____, whether he would recover.

A. Ekron   B. Edom   C. Ammon   D. Moab

557. Which prophet told Ahaziah's messengers that Ahaziah would die?

A. Elijah   B. Elisha   C. Micaiah   D. Haggai

558. What happened to the first captain—along with his men—who Ahaziah sent to capture Elijah?

A. They brought Elijah back   B. The Syrians attacked them
C. Fire from heaven killed them   D. They couldn't find Elijah

559. What happened to the second captain (as well as to his men) who Ahaziah sent to capture Elijah?

A. They brought Elijah back   B. The Syrians attacked them
C. Fire from heaven killed them   D. They couldn't find Elijah

560. What happened to the third group sent by Ahaziah to capture Elijah?

A. They brought Elijah back   B. The Syrians attacked them
C. Fire from heaven killed them   D. They couldn't find Elijah

561. How many days did the men of Jericho look for Elijah after he was taken up into heaven?

A. 1   B. 3   C. 7   D. They didn't look for him

562. Who was the king of Moab?

A. Zebah   B. Mesha   C. Baal   D. Joash

563. Jehoram, king of Israel, asked _____, king of Judah, to help him fight Moab.

A. Jehoshaphat   B. Ahab   C. Zimri   D. Hoshea

564. The king of what country joined them in fighting Moab?

A. Ammon   B. Syria   C. Edom   D. Egypt

565. When these kings needed water, which prophet was called?

A. Nathan   B. Micaiah   C. Elijah   D. Elisha

566. What did Elisha require before he prophesied?

A. A minstrel   B. A sacrifice   C. Quiet   D. Money

567. What did Elisha tell the three kings to do in order to get water?
A. Pray for rain   B. Offer a sacrifice to God   C. Dig a well
D. Dig ditches

568. The Moabites were defeated when they looked at the water in the ditches and thought it was what?
A. Mud   B. Blood   C. Dead bodies   D. Armor

569. When the king of Moab realized he was defeated, what did he offer as a burnt offering?
A. A bull   B. A lamb   C. His son   D. A pig

570. What did Elisha promise the Shunammite woman who had built a room for him?
A. Long life   B. A husband   C. Silver   D. A son

571. What happened to the Shunammite's son?
A. He died   B. He became God's prophet   C. He became king
D. He served in the temple

572. What happened to the Shunammite's son when Gehazi, Elisha's servant, laid Elisha's staff on his face?
A. He came back to life   B. Nothing   C. He blinked
D. He sneezed

573. What did the Shunammite's son do seven times, after Elisha laid on him?
A. He thanked Elisha   B. He hugged his mother   C. He blinked
D. He sneezed

574. Who was telling the king of Israel all of Syria's plans?
A. Isaiah   B. Gehazi   C. Elijah   D. Elisha

575. What kind of special chariots did Elisha's servant see?
A. Chariots of gold   B. Chariots of iron   C. Chariots of fire
D. Chariots of silver

576. What happened to the Syrians who were trying to capture Elisha?
A. They went back to Syria   B. They were attacked by Judah
C. They were struck blind   D. They were struck by lightning

577. To what city did Elisha lead the Syrians?
A. Samaria   B. Jerusalem   C. Dan   D. Shiloh

578. What did the king of Israel do to the Syrians?
A. He sent them home   B. He had them all killed
C. He made them slaves   D. He imprisoned them

579. When Samaria was undergoing a famine, whom did the king of Israel want to kill?

A. Ben-hadad   B. Elisha   C. Elijah   D. Isaiah

580. When Elisha predicted an abundance of food, who doubted him?

A. The king   B. A lord   C. The princes   D. His servant

581. Who found the Syrians' camp abandoned?

A. The king   B. Elisha   C. Four lepers   D. Two princes

582. As the Israelites rushed for the Syrians' food, who did they trample to death?

A. Elisha   B. Four lepers   C. The king   D. A lord

583. Elisha sent a prophet to anoint whom as king?

A. Josiah   B. Jehu   C. Joash   D. Joram

584. Which king of Israel did Jehu kill?

A. Joram   B. Ahab   C. Jehoshaphat   D. Asa

585. Who was Jehu's captain?

A. Baruch   B. Ithamar   C. Bidkar   D. Elon

586. Jehu had what king of Judah killed?

A. Rehoboam   B. Ezra   C. Joash   D. Ahaziah

587. What woman did Jehu have killed?

A. Jezebel   B. Esther   C. Athaliah   D. Ruth

588. Jehu killed all of Ahab's family, fulfilling whose prophecy?

A. Elisha's   B. Isaiah's   C. Elijah's   D. Joshua's

589. Jehu commanded his men to kill all the worshipers of whom?

A. The Lord   B. Molech   C. Asherah   D. Baal

590. God rewarded Jehu by saying that his children of the _____ generation would rule Israel.

A. Second   B. Third   C. Fourth   D. Fifth

591. Athaliah killed all the heirs to the throne except for whom?

A. Joash   B. Joram   C. Jeremiah   D. Joel

592. How old was Joash (Jehoash) when he began to rule Judah?

A. 5   B. 7   C. 13   D. 21

593. Who was the priest who instructed Joash (Jehoash)?

A. Eli   B. Zechariah   C. Jehoiada   D. Eleazar

594. Who made a hole in the chest that would hold money given to repair the temple?

A. Elisha   B. Elijah   C. Joash   D. Jehoiada

595. Joash paid _____, king of Syria, to leave Jerusalem.

A. Ben-hadad   B. Nimrod   C. Hazael   D. Necho

596. Who scolded Joash for turning to idolatry?

A. Jehoiada   B. Zechariah   C. Nahum   D. Iddo

597. Whose son was Zechariah?

A. Jehu's   B. Joash's   C. Jehoiada's   D. Jason's

598. What did Joash do to Zechariah?

A. He made him high priest   B. He imprisoned him
C. He had him killed   D. He exiled him

599. Israel's king, Joash, went to which prophet for help with the Syrians?

A. Isaiah   B. Elisha   C. Jeremiah   D. Elijah

600. What did Elisha tell Joash to do with the arrows?

A. Shoot them   B. Give them to Elisha
C. Hit them on the ground   D. Throw them out the window

601. How many times did Joash hit the arrows on the ground?

A. 1   B. 3   C. 7   D. 11

602. What did Elisha say the three times signified?

A. Israel would defeat Syria 3 times
B. Joash would die in 3 days   C. Syria would defeat Israel 3 times
D. Elisha would die in 3 days

603. What is Azariah's other name?

A. Uzziah   B. Uriah   C. Hezekiah   D. Ezra

604. What disease did King Uzziah have?

A. Palsy   B. Dropsy   C. Leprosy   D. Paralysis

605. The Israelites were transported from Israel to where?

A. Egypt   B. Syria   C. Assyria   D. Persia

606. The Assyrians put strangers in Israel's cities and some were killed by what?

A. Lions   B. The Samaritans   C. The Jews   D. Hailstones

607. Who spread the Assyrians' threatening letter before the Lord?

A. Josiah   B. Isaiah   C. Hezekiah   D. Jeremiah

608. What prophetess told of Jerusalem's coming destruction?
    A. Esther   B. Iddo   C. Huldah   D. Ruth

609. Josiah commanded the people to celebrate which feast?
    A. Passover   B. Pentecost   C. Trumpets   D. Firstfruits

610. Josiah was killed in a battle with what nation?
    A. Assyria   B. Egypt   C. Babylon   D. Syria

611. Who was Nebuchadnezzar's captain?
    A. Baruch   B. Gilgal   C. Nimrod   D. Nebuzar-adan

612. In Ezra the inhabitants who opposed the Jews (who had returned from the captivity) made trouble by writing to what king?
    A. Artaxerxes   B. Xerxes   C. Cyrus   D. Alexander

613. What was the king's reply?
    A. Continue building the temple   B. Imprison Ezra
    C. Proclaim a fast   D. Stop building the temple

614. After the Jews began again to rebuild the temple, their adversaries sent a letter to whom?
    A. Ezra   B. Darius   C. Cyrus   D. Artaxerxes

615. What was Darius's reply to this letter?
    A. Stop building the temple   B. Prepare for war
    C. Continue building the temple   D. Imprison Ezra

616. Tobiah mocked Nehemiah and the Jews by saying a _____ could knock down the wall they were building.
    A. Child   B. Fly   C. Horse   D. Fox

617. Nehemiah urged the people to stop what?
    A. Charging usury   B. Worshiping idols   C. Leaving
    D. Writing to the king

618. Who was Nehemiah's brother?
    A. Ezra   B. Geshem   C. Daniel   D. Hanani

619. Who read the book of the law to the people?
    A. Cyrus   B. Ezra   C. Zerubbabel   D. Nehemiah

620. The people were told, "The _____ of the LORD is your strength."
    A. Love   B. Peace   C. Faith   D. Joy

621. Whose possessions did Nehemiah throw from the temple?
    A. Sanballat's   B. Tobiah's   C. Geshem's   D. Ezra's

622. What man lived in the land of Uz?
A. Job   B. Joab   C. Isaiah   D. Jeremiah

623. How many children did Job have?
A. 3   B. 10   C. 6   D. 27

624. How many sheep did Job have?
A. 1,500   B. 3,000   C. 5,000   D. 7,000

625. How many camels did Job have?
A. 3,000   B. 1,000   C. 5,000   D. 700

626. How many yoke of oxen did Job have?
A. 500   B. 1,000   C. 300   D. 250

627. How many donkeys did Job have?
A. 300   B. 500   C. 100   D. 1,100

628. One of Job's visitors was called _____ the Temanite.
A. Eliphaz   B. Elihu   C. Zophar   D. Bildad

629. Another of Job's friends was _____ the Shuhite.
A. Eliphaz   B. Elihu   C. Zophar   D. Bildad

630. Job's third friend was _____ the Naamathite.
A. Eliphaz   B. Elihu   C. Zophar   D. Bildad

631. How many times did Eliphaz speak?
A. 1   B. 2   C. 3   D. 4

632. How many times did Bildad speak?
A. 1   B. 2   C. 3   D. 4

633. How many times did Zophar speak?
A. 1   B. 2   C. 3   D. 4

634. Who joined the conversation?
A. Samuel   B. Job's wife   C. Eli   D. Elihu

635. Job said of God, "Though he _____ me, yet will I trust in him."
A. Slay   B. Afflict   C. Ignore   D. Stone

636. Job said, "I know that my _____ liveth."
A. Soul   B. Redeemer   C. Children   D. Wife

637. Who was Jemima?
A. Job's wife   B. Eliphaz's wife   C. Job's daughter
D. Eliphaz's daughter

638. We read in Psalms that "the _____ declare the glory of God."
A. Prophets   B. Angels   C. Animals   D. Heavens

639. "The Lord is my shepherd" begins which psalm?
A. 18   B. 23   C. 51   D. 100

640. Which psalm did Moses write?
A. 15   B. 90   C. 100   D. 150

641. Which psalm is the shortest chapter in the Bible?
A. 23   B. 70   C. 100   D. 117

642. Which psalm is the longest chapter in the Bible?
A. 85   B. 100   C. 119   D. 147

643. How many verses does Psalm 119 have?
A. 66   B. 100   C. 150   D. 176

644. "There is a way which seemeth right unto a man," reads the proverb, "but the end thereof are the ways of _____."
A. Death   B. The world   C. Poverty   D. Destruction

645. "There is a friend that sticketh closer than a _____."
A. Garment   B. Child   C. Brother   D. Mother

646. "The beauty of old men is _____."
A. Their wives   B. The grey head   C. Experience   D. Knowledge

647. "Where there is no _____, the people perish."
A. Leader   B. Food   C. Wisdom   D. Vision

648. "Who can find a virtuous woman? For her price is far above _____."
A. Gold   B. Silver   C. Diamonds   D. Rubies

649. Who wrote Ecclesiastes?
A. David   B. Solomon   C. Isaiah   D. Samuel

650. Who wrote the "Song of Songs"?
A. Samuel   B. David   C. Solomon   D. Jeremiah

651. Who was Isaiah's father?
A. Hilkiah   B. Jonah   C. Amoz   D. Joab

652. "Though your sins be as scarlet, they shall be as white as _____."
A. Snow   B. Wool   C. The sun   D. Cotton

653. "Thou wilt keep him in perfect _____, whose mind is stayed on thee."
A. Health   B. Love   C. Prosperity   D. Peace

654. Isaiah predicted that what king would allow Jerusalem and the temple to be rebuilt?

A. Nebuchadnezzar   B. Cyrus   C. Darius   D. Ahab

655. Isaiah 53 speaks of Christ's what?

A. Birth   B. Resurrection   C. Sufferings   D. Ascension

656. Who was Jeremiah's father?

A. Amoz   B. Josiah   C. Ehud   D. Hilkiah

657. Jeremiah was from what city?

A. Bethlehem   B. Anathoth   C. Shiloh   D. Jericho

658. God told Jeremiah to hide a girdle by what river?

A. Euphrates   B. Nile   C. Jordan   D. Arnon

659. God said He wouldn't change His mind about Judah, even if Moses and _____ pleaded with Him.

A. Aaron   B. Samuel   C. David   D. Jeremiah

660. Who put Jeremiah in the stocks?

A. Jehoiada   B. God   C. Pashur   D. Manasseh

661. Jeremiah predicted that Pashur would die in what city?

A. Babylon   B. Jerusalem   C. Samaria   D. Jericho

662. The Lord showed Jeremiah two baskets of what?

A. Apples   B. Wheat   C. Corn   D. Figs

663. Which minor prophet is mentioned in the book of Jeremiah?

A. Haggai   B. Micah   C. Jonah   D. Amos

664. Jehoiakim killed which prophet?

A. Jeremiah   B. Isaiah   C. Urijah   D. Elijah

665. A false prophet, Hananiah, predicted the captives would return in how many years?

A. 2   B. 10   C. 15   D. 25

666. Who took a yoke off Jeremiah's neck and broke the yoke?

A. Jeremiah   B. Zedekiah   C. Hananiah   D. God

667. Jeremiah predicted Hananiah would die when?

A. In 2 years   B. In 5 years   C. In 3 years   D. That same year

668. Jeremiah bought a field in what city?

A. Bethlehem   B. Anathoth   C. Jerusalem   D. Hebron

669. What group of people refused to drink the wine Jeremiah had given them?

A. Chaldeans   B. Priests   C. Pharisees   D. Rechabites

670. What did King Jehoiakim do to Jeremiah's scroll of prophecies?

A. He burned it   B. He read it   C. He hid it   D. He buried it

671. What was in the dungeon Jeremiah was put in?

A. Rats   B. Mire   C. Skeletons   D. Straw

672. Who rescued Jeremiah from the dungeon?

A. Gabriel   B. Baruch   C. Josiah   D. Ebed-melech

673. What nationality was Ebed-melech?

A. Egyptian   B. Syrian   C. Ethiopian   D. Babylonian

674. Who killed the governor, Gedaliah?

A. Jeremiah   B. Nebuchadnezzar   C. God   D. Ishmael

675. Ezekiel saw creatures that had how many faces?

A. 2   B. 3   C. 4   D. 5

676. God had set Ezekiel as a what?

A. Deliverer   B. Shepherd   C. Watchman   D. Beacon

677. Ezekiel spoke of two sisters, Aholah and whom?

A. Aholibah   B. Sodom   C. Esther   D. Elah

678. Aholah represented what city?

A. Jericho   B. Samaria   C. Jerusalem   D. Babylon

679. Aholibah represented what city?

A. Jericho   B. Samaria   C. Jerusalem   D. Babylon

680. Which of Ezekiel's relatives died?

A. His wife   B. His son   C. His daughter   D. His mother

681. We read in the Book of Daniel that Belteshazzar's other name was what?

A. Shadrach   B. Meshach   C. Abednego   D. Daniel

682. What was Shadrach's other name?

A. Hananiah   B. Mishael   C. Azariah   D. Asa

683. What was Meshach's other name?

A. Hananiah   B. Mishael   C. Azariah   D. Asa

684. What was Abednego's other name?

A. Hananiah   B. Mishael   C. Azariah   D. Asa

685. Daniel's food experiment lasted how many days?
A. 3   B. 7   C. 10   D. 21

686. Nebuchadnezzar was going to kill what group of people?
A. Jews   B. Slaves   C. Persians   D. Wise men

687. Who dreamed of a huge tree that was cut down?
A. Nebuchadnezzar   B. Daniel   C. Shadrach   D. Cyrus

688. Who did this tree represent?
A. Nebuchadnezzar   B. Daniel   C. God   D. Cyrus

689. Who was "weighed in the balances, and . . . found wanting"?
A. Daniel   B. Belshazzar   C. Nebuchadnezzar   D. Darius

690. Daniel had a dream about four beasts. The first was like what animal?
A. Bear   B. Goat   C. Lion   D. Leopard

691. The second beast was like what animal?
A. Bear   B. Goat   C. Lion   D. Leopard

692. The third beast was like what animal?
A. Bear   B. Goat   C. Lion   D. Leopard

693. The fourth beast had 10 what?
A. Eyes   B. Horns   C. Heads   D. Feet

694. What came up in the middle of the 10 horns?
A. A little horn   B. A bump   C. Hair   D. A rock

695. Daniel had another vision in which the kings of Media and Persia were represented by what animal?
A. Lion   B. Goat   C. Ram   D. Leopard

696. What animal represented the king of Greece?
A. Bull   B. Lion   C. Ram   D. Goat

697. Who explained this vision to Daniel?
A. Michael   B. Gabriel   C. Cyrus   D. God

698. Daniel understood Judah's captivity would last 70 years by reading which prophet?
A. Jeremiah   B. Isaiah   C. Ezekiel   D. Jonah

699. Who was Hosea's first son?
A. Jezebel   B. Jezreel   C. Jerusalem   D. Jacob

700. Who was Hosea's daughter?
A. Athaliah   B. Jodab   C. Zimri   D. Lo-ruhamah

701. Who was Hosea's second son?

A. Jotham   B. Lo-ammi   C. Zeresh   D. Joshua

702. What priest opposed Amos?

A. Jehoiada   B. Aaron   C. Ezra   D. Amaziah

703. What gave Jonah shade from the sun?

A. A wall   B. A gourd   C. A cloud   D. A tent

704. What happened to the gourd?

A. Jonah cut it down   B. The horses trampled it
C. The wind blew it over   D. A worm killed it

705. Micah states, "What doth the LORD require of thee, but to do justly, and to love _____, and to walk humbly with thy God?"

A. Righteousness   B. Thy neighbor   C. Mercy   D. Peace

706. Zechariah saw which priest clothed in dirty garments?

A. Joshua   B. Aaron   C. Samuel   D. Eli

707. Zechariah states, "Not by might, nor by power, but by my _____, saith the LORD of hosts."

A. Strong arm   B. Spirit   C. Son   D. Strength

708. Zechariah had two staffs called Beauty and _____.

A. Holy   B. Israel   C. Bands   D. Bad

709. Malachi predicted that which prophet would precede the coming of Christ?

A. Moses   B. Isaiah   C. Elisha   D. Elijah

710. How many generations does Matthew list from Abraham to Christ?

A. 24   B. 42   C. 56   D. 100

711. Herod killed the children of Bethlehem that were _____ years old or younger.

A. 2   B. 3   C. 4   D. 5

712. Mary, Joseph, and Jesus were in Egypt until the death of whom?

A. Pharaoh   B. Caesar   C. Herod   D. Joseph

713. Archelaus was whose son?

A. Caesar's   B. Pharoah's   C. Joseph's   D. Herod's

714. Who wore camel's hair, and ate locusts and wild honey?

A. Jesus   B. John the Baptist   C. Peter   D. Herod

715. John baptized people in what river?

A. Euphrates   B. Jordan   C. Nile   D. Tigris

716. Who told Jesus, "I have need to be baptized of thee"?
A. John the Baptist   B. Peter   C. James   D. Herod

717. Jesus said to put our treasure where?
A. Under a bushel   B. In the earth   C. In heaven   D. In a bank

718. The people were amazed at Jesus' teaching, because He taught with authority and not as whom?
A. John the Baptist   B. The Pharisees   C. The Priests
D. The scribes

719. Who said, "Lord, if thou wilt, thou canst make me clean"?
A. John   B. A leper   C. Jairus   D. A scribe

720. Jesus marveled at what Roman's faith?
A. Pilate's   B. Herod's   C. A centurion's   D. Caesar's

721. To whom did Jesus say, "The foxes have holes, and the birds of the air have nests; but the Son of man hath not where to lay his head"?
A. A scribe   B. Peter   C. John the Baptist   D. Andrew

722. After Jesus cast demons into some pigs, what happened to the pigs?
A. They were slaughtered   B. They drowned in the sea
C. Nothing   D. They were struck by lightning

723. After the citizens heard about the pigs, what did they ask Jesus to do?
A. Leave   B. Heal their sick   C. Preach to them   D. Do a miracle

724. The disciples of John the Baptist said they and the Pharisees did something that Jesus' disciples didn't do. What was it?
A. Prayed   B. Washed their hands   C. Fasted   D. Gave alms

725. "The harvest truly is plenteous, but the _____ are few."
A. Days   B. Disciples   C. Concerned   D. Labourers

726. Jesus told his disciples to be as wise as _____, and harmless as doves.
A. Owls   B. Foxes   C. Serpents   D. Wolves

727. Jesus said John the Baptist was which Old Testament prophet?
A. Isaiah   B. Elijah   C. Moses   D. Elisha

728. Jesus said Sodom had a better chance in the day of judgment than which city?
A. Capernaum   B. Jerusalem   C. Nazareth   D. Babylon

729. Jesus said that blasphemy against whom could not be forgiven?
A. Himself   B. The Father   C. The Holy Ghost   D. One's parents

730. In the parable of the sower, Jesus first mentions that some seed fell where?

A. On good ground   B. On stony ground   C. By the wayside
D. Among thorns

731. Secondly, Jesus said some seed fell where?

A. On good ground   B. On stony ground   C. By the wayside
D. Among thorns

732. The third place the seed fell was where?

A. On good ground   B. On stony ground   C. By the wayside
D. Among thorns

733. The fourth place the seed fell was where?

A. On good ground   B. On stony ground   C. By the wayside
D. Among thorns

734. Jesus said that a man sowed a field of wheat but an enemy planted what among the wheat?

A. Discord   B. Weeds   C. Tares   D. Oats

735. Who was the enemy that sowed the tares?

A. The Pharisees   B. Pride   C. Jealousy   D. The devil

736. Who sowed the wheat?

A. The Son of man   B. The disciples   C. The law   D. Peter

737. Who are the reapers of the harvest?

A. The disciples   B. Jesus   C. Angels   D. Good men

738. What did Jesus say is the "least of all seeds"?

A. The acorn   B. Faith   C. The mustard seed   D. Love

739. Jesus said to a Gentile woman, "It is not meet to take the children's bread, and to cast it to _____."

A. Strangers   B. Dogs   C. Swine   D. Gentiles

740. To whom did Jesus say, "Get thee behind me, Satan"?

A. Thomas   B. Judas   C. The Pharisees   D. Peter

741. Jesus asked, "What shall a man give in exchange for his _____?"

A. Soul   B. Life   C. Health   D. Wisdom

742. Jesus told Peter, James, and John to tell no one of His transfiguration until after His _____.

A. Death   B. Resurrection   C. Ascension   D. Second coming

743. Jesus told the disciples that they could not cast out a demon from a boy because of their _____.

A. Inexperience   B. Education   C. Unbelief   D. Ignorance

744. Jesus said that faith as a grain of mustard seed could move what?

A. Sinners   B. The temple   C. The sea   D. A mountain

745. When Peter found money in a fish's mouth he paid what?

A. For food   B. His taxes   C. For the fish   D. Jesus

746. Peter asked Jesus whether _____ times was enough to forgive his brother.

A. 3   B. 5   C. 7   D. 10

747. Jesus told a parable of a servant who owed the king _____ talents.

A. 1,000   B. 10,000   C. 100,000   D. 200,000

748. But this forgiven servant did not forgive one who owed him _____ pence.

A. 10   B. 50   C. 100   D. 150

749. Who came "to give his life a ransom for many"?

A. John the Baptist   B. Jesus   C. Paul   D. James

750. Jesus healed two blind men near what city?

A. Jerusalem   B. Capernaum   C. Bethany   D. Jericho

751. As Jesus rode into Jerusalem, the people cried out, saying "_____ to the son of David."

A. Hosanna   B. Hallelujah   C. Glory, honor, and majesty   D. Abba

752. After Jesus' triumphal entry into Jerusalem, in which city did He spend the night?

A. Bethany   B. Bethlehem   C. Jerusalem   D. Emmaus

753. What group asked Jesus about paying taxes?

A. Romans   B. Jews   C. Herodians   D. Disciples

754. Which group did not believe in the resurrection from the dead?

A. Pharisees   B. Disciples   C. Herodians   D. Sadducees

755. The Sadducees asked Jesus about a woman who married _____ brothers.

A. 2   B. 3   C. 5   D. 7

756. When asked, the Pharisees said that Christ was whose son?

A. God's   B. David's   C. Abraham's   D. Joseph's

757. Jesus told His disciples that the greatest of them would be what?

A. A servant   B. An apostle   C. A leader   D. A prophet

758. Chapter 23 of Matthew describes what group as hypocrites?

A. The disciples   B. The Sadducees   C. The publicans
D. The Pharisees

759. Jesus said the Pharisees "strain at a gnat, and swallow a _____."

A. Dove   B. Sparrow   C. Horse   D. Camel

760. Jesus also said that the Pharisees were like "whited _____."

A. Sepulchres   B. Fences   C. Crosses   D. Barns

761. Jesus told a parable about _____ virgins.

A. 2   B. 5   C. 10   D. 12

762. How many of these virgins were wise?

A. 2   B. 5   C. 7   D. 10

763. When did the bridegroom come?

A. The sixth hour   B. The ninth hour   C. The eleventh hour
D. Midnight

764. In the parable of the talents, how many talents was the first servant given?

A. 1   B. 2   C. 5   D. 10

765. The second servant received how many talents?

A. 1   B. 2   C. 5   D. 10

766. The third servant received how many talents?

A. 1   B. 2   C. 5   D. 10

767. How many talents did the first servant gain?

A. 0   B. 1   C. 2   D. 5

768. How many talents did the second servant gain?

A. 0   B. 1   C. 2   D. 5

769. How many talents did the third servant gain?

A. 0   B. 1   C. 2   D. 5

770. Who received the wicked servant's one talent?

A. The Lord   B. The first servant   C. The second servant
D. No one

771. When Jesus separated the sheep and goats, who was on His right hand?

A. God   B. The goats   C. The disciples   D. The sheep

772. At His arrest, Jesus said the Father would give Him how many legions of angels?

A. 3   B. 7   C. 12   D. 20

773. After Peter heard this, he wept bitterly. What did he hear?

A. Jesus' voice   B. A rooster crow   C. The sound of a whip
D. The last trump

774. After Jesus cried out on the cross, some thought He was trying to call which prophet?

A. Elijah   B. Isaiah   C. Moses   D. Elisha

775. Many bodies of the saints came out of their graves after Jesus' _____.

A. Ascension   B. Death   C. Resurrection   D. Burial

776. In whose tomb was Jesus buried?

A. His own   B. Nicodemus's   C. Peter's   D. Joseph's

777. Who rolled the stone away from Jesus' tomb?

A. An angel   B. The guards   C. The disciples   D. The women

778. After His resurrection, Jesus met the disciples on a mountain in _____.

A. Judea   B. Galilee   C. Nazareth   D. Perea

779. Mark reports in his Gospel that a man sick of the palsy was carried to Jesus by how many men?

A. 1   B. 2   C. 3   D. 4

780. What did they do so they could get the sick man to Jesus?

A. They pushed the crowd aside
B. They asked Jesus to come out
C. They lowered the sick man down from the roof
D. They shouted "Hallelujah"

781. What did Jesus say to the sick man that offended the scribes?

A. Go and sin no more   B. You are free from the law
C. Thy sins be forgiven thee   D. Trust in me

782. When the multitudes thronged Jesus, He taught from what?

A. A pulpit   B. A ship   C. A mountain   D. An altar

783. Who was the man who lived among the tombs?

A. Legion   B. Lazarus   C. John the Baptist   D. Hiram

784. To whom was Jesus referring when He said, "The damsel is not dead, but sleepeth"?

A. Martha   B. Mary Magdalene   C. Salome   D. Jairus's daughter

785. When Herod heard of Jesus, he thought Jesus was _____, risen from the dead?

A. Elijah   B. Moses   C. John the Baptist   D. David

786. What did Herodias's daughter want as a reward for pleasing Herod?

A. Half the kingdom   B. The head of John the Baptist
C. A husband   D. The royal palace at Caesarea

787. Jesus said evil thoughts came from where?

A. The mind   B. The brain   C. Lust   D. The heart

788. In healing one man Jesus said, "Ephphatha," meaning what?

A. Thy will be done   B. Sin no more   C. Be opened
D. Peace, be still

789. Why did Jesus spit on a man in Bethsaida?

A. The man had spit on Jesus   B. Because of his unbelief
C. He had cursed Jesus   D. Jesus was healing him

790. Which two disciples asked Jesus to sit at His right hand and left hand?

A. Peter and Andrew   B. James and John   C. Peter and John
D. Andrew and Thomas

791. How many mites did the poor widow put in the treasury?

A. 1   B. 2   C. 3   D. 4

792. Two mites equal one what?

A. Penny   B. Gerah   C. Peck   D. Farthing

793. Jesus said that which prophet spoke of the "abomination of desolation"?

A. Isaiah   B. Jeremiah   C. Ezekiel   D. Daniel

794. To whom did Luke address his gospel?

A. Theophilus   B. Tiberius   C. Peter   D. Mary

795. An angel told Mary that Jesus would sit on whose throne?

A. God's   B. His own throne   C. David's   D. Solomon's

796. Who did Mary visit?

A. Hannah   B. Elisabeth   C. Anna   D. Simeon

797. What was Elisabeth's son first called?

A. Zacharias   B. Saul   C. John   D. Samuel

798. When he was 12, Jesus accompanied His parents to what feast?

A. Pentecost   B. Trumpets   C. Tabernacles   D. Passover

799. How many days did Mary and Joseph look for the lost Jesus?

A. 2   B. 3   C. 4   D. 5

800. Which Caesar was reigning when John the Baptist began his ministry?
A. Julius   B. Claudius   C. Tiberius   D. Augustus

801. John said God could raise up children to Abraham from what?
A. Dust   B. Stones   C. Corpses   D. Bread

802. John told whom to be content with their wages?
A. Soldiers   B. Tax collectors   C. Pharisees   D. Scribes

803. In Luke's genealogy, who was called the son of God?
A. Jesus   B. Abraham   C. David   D. Adam

804. Who led Jesus into the wilderness to be tempted?
A. Satan   B. The Holy Spirit   C. God   D. An angel

805. People from what city tried to throw Jesus down a hill?
A. Nazareth   B. Jerusalem   C. Capernaum   D. Cana

806. Who came "neither eating bread nor drinking wine" and the people thought he had a devil?
A. Peter   B. Matthew   C. Jesus   D. John the Baptist

807. James and John wanted to call down fire from heaven like which Old Testament prophet?
A. Moses   B. Elijah   C. Elisha   D. Isaiah

808. Whose blood had Pilate mingled with their sacrifices?
A. The Galileans   B. The Jews   C. The Samaritans   D. The Romans

809. The tower of Siloam fell and killed how many people?
A. 7   B. 13   C. 18   D. 22

810. Jesus healed a woman who had a "spirit of infirmity" for how many years?
A. 7   B. 13   C. 18   D. 22

811. Jesus said before you build what, you should see whether you have enough money to finish it?
A. A house.   B. A city.   C. A stable   D. A tower

812. Jesus said, "Ye cannot serve God and _____."
A. Yourself   B. Mammon   C. Sin   D. Satan

813. Who said, "God be merciful to me a sinner"?
A. Peter   B. Zacchaeus   C. A Pharisee   D. A publican

814. Who strengthened Jesus during His agony in the Garden of Gethsemane?
A. God   B. An angel   C. The Holy Spirit   D. Peter, James, and John

815. One of the two men who Jesus appeared to on the road to Emmaus was named what?

A. Cleopas   B. Alexander   C. Simeon   D. Annas

816. The Gospel of John tells us that Philip was from what city?

A. Capernaum   B. Bethsaida   C. Jerusalem   D. Cana

817. Jesus saw Nathanael under what kind of tree?

A. Fig   B. Olive   C. Sycamore   D. Cedar

818. After Jesus turned the water into wine at Cana, who was the first to taste it?

A. The bride   B. The groom   C. The governor of the feast   D. Jesus

819. Jesus said, "Destroy this temple, and in _____ days I will raise it up."

A. 3   B. 7   C. 40   D. 120

820. The Jews said that it took how many years to build the temple?

A. 28   B. 46   C. 63   D. 70

821. Nicodemus was from which Jewish group?

A. Sadducees   B. Essenes   C. Pharisees   D. Herodians

822. Near what city was Jacob's well located?

A. Jerusalem   B. Sychar   C. Capernaum   D. Bethany

823. What did Jesus offer the woman at the well?

A. The bread of life   B. Rest   C. Money   D. Living water

824. Jesus said that they who worship God must worship Him "in spirit and in _____."

A. Faith   B. Love   C. Truth   D. Body

825. Jesus said, "For had ye believed _____, ye would have believed me: for he wrote of me."

A. David   B. Abraham   C. God   D. Moses

826. Because many people believed in Jesus because of this man, the Jews wanted to put whom to death?

A. Lazarus   B. Peter   C. Nicodemus   D. John the Baptist

827. Who was Judas Iscariot's father?

A. Jonah   B. Simon   C. Peter   D. Joseph

828. Who washed the disciples' feet?

A. Judas   B. Peter   C. John   D. Jesus

829. Jesus said, "A new commandment give I unto you, That ye _____."

A. Forgive your enemies   B. Have faith   C. Love one another
D. Preach the Word

830. Jesus said, "I am the vine, ye are the _____."

A. Fruit   B. Branches   C. Husbandmen   D. Vines

831. At Jesus' trial, the Jews did not enter the hall of judgment because of what?

A. The passover   B. The priests   C. The soldiers   D. Pilate

832. Who said, "What I have written I have written"?

A. Jesus   B. John   C. Luke   D. Pilate

833. At first Mary Magdalene thought Jesus was whom?

A. An angel   B. The gardener   C. A soldier   D. Peter

834. When Jesus appeared to the disciples at the Sea of Galilee, how many fish did the disciples catch?

A. 40   B. 113   C. 153   D. 222

835. As told in the Book of Acts, one of the men nominated to take Judas's place was named Joseph or Barsabas or what other name?

A. Justus   B. Matthew   C. Levi   D. Joshua

836. On the day of Pentecost, Peter quoted Joel as saying that who would dream dreams?

A. Disciples   B. Young men   C. Old men   D. Daughters

837. Peter and John went up into the temple at the hour of prayer which was what hour?

A. Third   B. Sixth   C. Ninth   D. Twelfth

838. What other name did Barnabas go by?

A. Saul   B. Justus   C. Silas   D. Joses

839. Who was Sapphira's husband?

A. Barnabas   B. Ananias   C. Silas   D. Peter

840. The sick people hoped that whose shadow might fall on them so they could be healed?

A. Peter's   B. John's   C. Paul's   D. Philip's

841. Who spoke of Theudas and Judas, who had rebelled against Rome?

A. Pilate   B. Peter   C. Gamaliel   D. Paul

842. Of which crime was Stephen accused?

A. Murder   B. Theft   C. Adultery   D. Blasphemy

843. The men who stoned Stephen laid their coats at whose feet?

A. Stephen's   B. James's   C. Saul's   D. John's

844. What sorcerer was baptized under Philip's preaching?
A. Elymas B. Festus C. Agrippa D. Simon

845. Who tried to buy power from Peter?
A. Paul B. Simon C. Philip D. Levi

846. Whom did the church at Jerusalem send to Antioch?
A. Barnabas B. Luke C. Paul D. Peter

847. Whom did Barnabas bring to Antioch?
A. Silas B. Paul C. Luke D. Mark

848. Who predicted a famine would strike the land?
A. Peter B. Barnabas C. Paul D. Agabus

849. This prophecy was fulfilled during the reign of which Caesar?
A. Tiberius B. Nero C. Claudius D. Augustus

850. The church at Antioch sent aid with Barnabas and Paul for which land?
A. Galilee B. Judea C. Pontus D. Samaria

851. Who returned with Barnabas and Paul from Jerusalem?
A. John Mark B. Luke C. Matthew D. Justus

852. Who was the sorcerer Barnabas and Paul found on Cyprus?
A. Simon B. Justus C. Agabus D. Bar-Jesus

853. What was Bar-Jesus' other name?
A. Magus B. Elymas C. Simeon D. Aquila

854. Who told Elymas he would be blind?
A. Barnabas B. Mark C. Paul D. John

855. Who was sent to Antioch with Paul and Barnabas?
A. Peter and John B. Thomas and Matthew C. Judas and Silas
D. Mark and Luke

856. Lydia was originally from what city?
A. Laodicea B. Sardis C. Ephesus D. Thyatira

857. Who cast a spirit of divination out of a young girl?
A. Peter B. Paul C. Silas D. Barnabas

858. When Paul and Silas were in prison, who or what opened the doors of the prison?
A. The keeper B. An angel C. An earthquake D. Lightning

859. Who was about to kill himself?
A. The keeper of the prison B. Paul C. Silas D. Luke

860. The magistrates of Philippi were afraid upon learning that Paul and Silas were what?

A. Jews   B. Christians   C. Judeans   D. Romans

861. On what had Paul seen the inscription, "TO THE UNKNOWN GOD"?

A. A temple   B. An altar   C. A statue   D. An arena

862. In Corinth Paul met Aquila and Priscilla who had recently come from what city?

A. Jerusalem   B. Tarsus   C. Ephesus   D. Rome

863. Which Caesar commanded all the Jews to leave Rome?

A. Augustus   B. Tiberius   C. Claudius   D. Nero

864. The Jews started a riot at Corinth when who was the deputy of Achaia?

A. Pilate   B. Gallio   C. Nero   D. Ananias

865. When Gallio refused to hear the Jews, whom did they beat?

A. Gallio   B. Paul   C. Silas   D. Sosthenes

866. Because of a vow, Paul shaved his head in what city?

A. Corinth   B. Cenchrea   C. Jerusalem   D. Ephesus

867. From what city was Apollos?

A. Alexandria   B. Rome   C. Jerusalem   D. Ephesus

868. Who instructed Apollos more clearly in the way of God?

A. Paul   B. Peter   C. Aquila and Priscilla   D. Paul and Silas

869. At Ephesus the Holy Ghost came on twelve men, after who had laid his hands on them?

A. Apollos   B. Peter   C. Barnabas   D. Paul

870. At Ephesus Paul disputed "daily in the school of one _____."

A. Crispus   B. Tyrannus   C. Apollos   D. Silas

871. Sick people were healed when handkerchiefs were taken from whose body?

A. Paul's   B. Peter's   C. John's   D. Silas's

872. Seven sons of whom tried to cast out demons in Jesus' name?

A. Ananias   B. Demas   C. Sceva   D. Paul

873. The mob at Ephesus shouted for two hours when who tried to speak?

A. Paul   B. Apollos   C. Timothy   D. Alexander

874. Who finally quieted the mob?

A. Paul   B. Luke   C. The town clerk   D. Alexander

875. Paul hastened to Jerusalem to attend which feast?
    A. Passover   B. Pentecost   C. Hanukkah   D. Feast of Trumpets

876. Who predicted Paul would be bound at Jerusalem?
    A. Philip   B. Apollos   C. Paul   D. Agabus

877. At Jerusalem Paul and four other men were in the temple purifying themselves for how many days?
    A. 3   B. 7   C. 12   D. 40

878. Who rescued Paul from the mob at Jerusalem?
    A. The chief captain   B. An angel   C. Peter   D. Silas

879. Who was the chief captain?
    A. Tiberius   B. Sergius Paulus   C. Claudius Lysias   D. Julius

880. The Jews grew silent when Paul spoke what language?
    A. Hebrew   B. Greek   C. Latin   D. Egyptian

881. Who was the high priest at Paul's trial?
    A. Caiaphas   B. Judas   C. Pilate   D. Ananias

882. What two groups debated at Paul's trial?
    A. Jews and Romans   B. Pharisees and Sadducees
    C. Essenes and Pharisees   D. Herodians and Zealots

883. At Paul's trial who was Tertullus?
    A. The governor   B. The high priest   C. An orator   D. A centurion

884. On the trip to Rome, what centurion was in charge of Paul?
    A. Julius   B. Augustus   C. Festus   D. Lysias

885. How many people were on the ship going to Rome?
    A. 153   B. 276   C. 303   D. 500

886. When a snake bit Paul, the people of the island thought Paul must be what?
    A. A thief   B. A rebel   C. A murderer   D. A slave

887. When Paul did not die from the snake bite the people thought he must be a what?
    A. Murderer   B. God   C. Roman   D. Magician

888. Who was the chief man of the island?
    A. Publius   B. Cyrus   C. Julius   D. Festus

889. Which of Publius's relatives did Paul heal?
    A. Mother   B. Sister   C. Brother   D. Father

890. To what did Castor and Pollux refer?

A. Publius's sons   B. A ship   C. An altar   D. The wind

891. In Rome Paul lived in his own house for how many years?

A. 1   B. 2   C. 3   D. 4

892. In the Book of Romans, who said, "I am not ashamed of the gospel of Christ"?

A. Peter   B. John   C. Timothy   D. Paul

893. What Old Testament character does Paul use as an example of faith?

A. Adam   B. Samson   C. Abraham   D. Solomon

894. "For all have _____, and come short of the glory of God."

A. Sinned   B. Tried   C. Failed   D. Made mistakes

895. "For the wages of sin is _____."

A. Guilt   B. Hell   C. Death   D. Regret

896. To whom did Paul dictate the Book of Romans?

A. Timothy   B. Tertius   C. Titus   D. Luke

897. Which chapter in First Corinthians deals with charity (love)?

A. 7   B. 9   C. 12   D. 13

898. The main topic of First Corinthians 15 is what?

A. Suffering   B. Resurrection   C. Faith   D. Love

899. First Corinthians 15:22 states, "For as in _____ all die, even so in Christ shall all be made alive."

A. Adam   B. Sin   C. Satan   D. Vain

900. Second Corinthians 9:7 says, "God loveth a _____ giver."

A. Sincere   B. Dutiful   C. Cheerful   D. Faithful

901. Which apostle did Paul have to withstand?

A. Peter   B. James   C. John   D. Thomas

902. What does "Abba" mean?

A. Amen   B. So be it   C. Pray   D. Father

903. In Philippians Paul refers to Euodias and _____.

A. Titus   B. Syntyche   C. Aquilla   D. Silas

904. From which city was Epaphroditus?

A. Corinth   B. Ephesus   C. Colosse   D. Philippi

905. From which city was Epaphras?

A. Corinth   B. Ephesus   C. Colosse   D. Philippi

906. After the letter was read at Colosse, in what other city was it to be read?
A. Rome   B. Laodicea   C. Smyrna   D. Ephesus

907. Who was "the beloved physician"?
A. Paul   B. Mark   C. Luke   D. Barnabas

908. In First Timothy, Paul wrote that he had left Timothy in what city?
A. Athens   B. Rome   C. Corinth   D. Ephesus

909. Paul wrote that Jannes and Jambres had withstood whom?
A. Moses   B. David   C. Paul   D. Timothy

910. In which country had Paul left Titus?
A. Greece   B. Judea   C. Italy   D. Crete

911. Paul wrote to Philemon concerning his what?
A. Faith   B. Love   C. Mother   D. Slave

912. Who was Philemon's slave?
A. Epaphras   B. Onesimus   C. Titus   D. Demas

913. In Hebrews, who is said to be a priest after the order of Melchisedec?
A. Aaron   B. Samuel   C. Christ   D. Eli

914. In Hebrews 11, who is referred to by the words, "he being dead yet speaketh"?
A. David   B. Abraham   C. Isaac   D. Abel

915. In Hebrews 11, who "had this testimony, that he pleased God"?
A. Adam   B. Enoch   C. Noah   D. Abraham

916. Who is "the author and finisher of our faith"?
A. Jesus   B. God   C. Moses   D. Paul

917. James wrote, "the trying of your faith worketh _____."
A. Hope   B. Love   C. Patience   D. Glory

918. "Be ye doers of the word, and not _____ only."
A. Hearers   B. Speakers   C. Sitters   D. Believers

919. James wrote that "faith without _____ is dead."
A. Hope   B. Love   C. Sincerity   D. Works

920. "But the _____ can no man tame."
A. Wicked   B. Tongue   C. Woman   D. Devil

921. "Resist the _____, and he will flee from you."
A. Robber   B. Spirit   C. Devil   D. Fool

922. James wrote, "Ye have heard of the patience of _____."
A. Noah B. Jacob C. David D. Job

923. Who does Peter say walks about "seeking whom he may devour"?
A. Caesar B. The devil C. Gabriel D. Herod

924. Which apostle does Peter mention in his second epistle?
A. Paul B. John C. James D. Philip

925. To whom is John's third epistle addressed?
A. Luke B. Gaius C. Theophilus D. Paul

926. In III John, who did John say opposed him?
A. Demetrius B. Gaius C. Peter D. Diotrephes

927. Who was Jude's brother?
A. John B. Peter C. James D. Paul

928. In Revelation, John wrote to the seven churches of _____.
A. Europe B. Italy C. Asia D. Judea

929. These seven churches were represented by what?
A. 7 stars B. 7 candlesticks C. 7 trumpets D. 7 bowls

930. To which church was written, "thou hast left thy first love"?
A. Ephesus B. Philadelphia C. Smyrna D. Laodicea

931. Which church was warned about Jezebel?
A. Ephesus B. Thyatira C. Sardis D. Pergamos

932. Which church was called "lukewarm"?
A. Pergamos B. Smyrna C. Philadelphia D. Laodicea

933. How many elders sat around the throne of God?
A. 3 B. 7 C. 24 D. 40

934. How many lamps burned before the throne of God?
A. 3 B. 7 C. 24 D. 40

935. How many beasts cried, "Holy, holy, holy" to the Lord?
A. 4 B. 7 C. 12 D. 24

936. Each beast had how many wings?
A. 2 B. 4 C. 6 D. 8

937. God held a book sealed with how many seals?
A. 2 B. 4 C. 7 D. 10

938. The first seal revealed a horse of what color?
A. Red B. Brown C. Black D. White

939. The second seal revealed a horse of what color?
    A. Red   B. Brown   C. Black   D. White

940. The third seal revealed a horse of what color?
    A. Red   B. Brown   C. Black   D. White

941. What did the rider of the black horse have in his hand?
    A. A sword   B. Balances   C. A spear   D. A scroll

942. The fourth seal revealed a _____ horse.
    A. Brown   B. Bay   C. Black   D. Pale

943. Who sat on the pale horse?
    A. John   B. Jesus   C. Gabriel   D. Death

944. Who "followed with" Death?
    A. Hell   B. Satan   C. Suffering   D. Lucifer

945. The fifth seal revealed what?
    A. More horses   B. An army   C. Martyrs   D. Angels

946. What happened when the sixth seal was opened?
    A. An earthquake   B. The sun became black   C. Stars fell
    D. All of the above

947. How many people were sealed with the seal of God?
    A. 1,000   B. 40,000   C. 144,000   D. 1 billion

948. How many were sealed from each tribe of Israel?
    A. 2,000   B. 40,000   C. 10,000   D. 12,000

949. After the seventh seal was opened, there was silence in heaven for how long?
    A. Half an hour   B. 3 days   C. 7 years   D. 1,000 years

950. What fell on the earth after the first trumpet sounded?
    A. Lightning   B. Hail and fire   C. Rain   D. Blood

951. The second trumpet sounded and a mountain of fire fell on what?
    A. The earth   B. The sun   C. The rivers   D. The sea

952. The third trumpet sounded, and a star called _____ fell on the rivers.
    A. Apollyon   B. Cyrus   C. Wormwood   D. Death

953. The fourth trumpet sounded, and brought what?
    A. Intense heat   B. Pestilence   C. Frogs   D. Darkness

954. The fifth trumpet sounded, and brought what?
    A. Locusts   B. Hail   C. Lightning   D. Darkness

955. Who was king over the locusts?

A. Gabriel   B. Lucifer   C. Michael   D. Abaddon

956. What was his Greek name?

A. Marcus   B. Apollyon   C. Amos   D. Paulus

957. The sixth trumpet sounded, and an angel was ordered to loose four angels from which river?

A. Jordan   B. Nile   C. Euphrates   D. Tigris

958. How many million men were in their army?

A. 4   B. 70   C. 100   D. 200

959. John was forbidden to write what the 7 _____ uttered.

A. Angels   B. Beasts   C. Thunders   D. Elders

960. What did John do with the book the angel held?

A. He ate it   B. He read it   C. He copied it   D. He hid it

961. An angel told John that the Gentiles would tread the holy city for how many months?

A. 6   B. 18   C. 24   D. 42

962. Who will prophesy 1,260 days?

A. John   B. God's 2 witnesses   C. The Gentiles   D. The 144,000

963. God's 2 witnesses are represented by 2 candlesticks and 2 what?

A. Olive trees   B. Angels   C. Staffs   D. Lamps

964. Who will kill God's 2 witnesses?

A. An angel   B. The dragon   C. John   D. The beast

965. The bodies of God's 2 witnesses will lie in what city?

A. Rome   B. Babylon   C. Jerusalem   D. Ephesus

966. God's 2 witnesses will become alive in how many days?

A. 2   B. 3   C. 3½   D. 4½

967. After this, 7,000 people are killed by what?

A. An angel   B. An earthquake   C. Lightning   D. Hail

968. God's kingdom is announced by the seventh what?

A. Trumpet   B. Vial   C. Seal   D. Beast

969. John saw "a woman clothed with the sun" having a crown of 12 what?

A. Pearls   B. Diamonds   C. Stars   D. Rubies

970. Who fought a war in heaven with the dragon?

A. God   B. Jesus   C. Gabriel   D. Michael

971. Who is the dragon?

A. Antichrist   B. Gabriel   C. The beast   D. Satan

972. John saw a beast like a leopard, bear, and what?

A. A lion   B. An eagle   C. A ram   D. A goat

973. Who gives power to the beast?

A. The lion   B. The dragon   C. An angel   D. John

974. The beast has power for how many months?

A. 3   B. 12   C. 24   D. 42

975. John saw another beast that had 2 horns like what?

A. A lamb   B. A bull   C. A dragon   D. A goat

976. Who told people to make an image of the first beast?

A. The first beast   B. The dragon   C. The second beast
D. An angel

977. The second beast made the image what?

A. Fall   B. Walk   C. Crumble   D. Speak

978. No one could buy or sell unless they had the number of whom?

A. The first beast   B. The second beast   C. The dragon   D. God

979. What is the number of the beast?

A. 163   B. 377   C. 666   D. 888

980. Seven angels received 7 "golden _____ full of the wrath of God."

A. Rings   B. Vials   C. Trumpets   D. Scrolls

981. The first vial was poured on the earth and brought what?

A. Sores   B. Darkness   C. Locusts   D. Earthquakes

982. The second vial was poured on the sea and it became what?

A. Stormy   B. Dark   C. Blood   D. Calm

983. The third vial was poured out where?

A. In the air   B. On the earth   C. On the sun   D. On the rivers

984. The fourth vial was poured out on the sun and it what?

A. Became dark   B. Turned blood red   C. Scorched men
D. Fell from the sky

985. The fifth vial was poured out and brought what?

A. Darkness   B. An earthquake   C. Hail   D. Sores

986. The sixth vial was poured out on what river?

A. Jordan   B. Euphrates   C. Nile   D. Tigris

987. The Euphrates River was dried up to prepare the way for the kings of the
_____.

    A. East   B. West   C. North   D. South

988. The seventh vial was poured out and brought what?

    A. Darkness   B. An earthquake   C. Sores   D. A flood

989. Also what fell from heaven?

    A. Rain   B. Stars   C. Hail   D. Snow

990. The merchants mourned over the destruction of what city?

    A. Rome   B. Jerusalem   C. Ephesus   D. Babylon

991. John saw Jesus sitting on what color horse?

    A. White   B. Black   C. Red   D. Brown

992. An angel cast the devil into the bottomless pit for how many years?

    A. 100   B. 500   C. 700   D. 1,000

993. What city did John see coming down from heaven?

    A. New Babylon   B. New Jerusalem   C. New Bethlehem
    D. New Rome

994. New Jerusalem had how many gates?

    A. 1   B. 2   C. 4   D. 12

995. Who stood beside the gates?

    A. Angels   B. Apostles   C. Elders   D. Seraphim

996. Each gate had the name of _____.

    A. An angel   B. An apostle   C. A tribe of Israel   D. God

997. Each gate was made of what?

    A. Diamonds   B. Pearls   C. Gold   D. Silver

998. The wall of New Jerusalem had how many foundations?

    A. 3   B. 6   C. 9   D. 12

999. The foundations had the names of what?

    A. Angels   B. Apostles   C. Tribes of Israel   D. God

1000. The street of New Jerusalem is made of what?

    A. Gold   B. Silver   C. Pearls   D. Diamonds

1001. The tree of life bore how many kinds of fruit?

    A. 1   B. 2   C. 4   D. 12

Answers and References

131. D. Gen. 30:9-13
132. B. Gen. 30:20-21
133. A. Gen. 30:22-24;
     35:16-18
134. C. Gen. 31:19
135. C. Gen. 31:41
136. C. Gen. 31:41
137. A. Gen. 32:24-30
138. D. Gen. 32:25
139. B. Gen. 34:8
140. A. Gen. 34:2
141. C. Gen. 34:25-26
142. A. Gen. 35:18-19
143. D. Gen. 35:28
144. C. Gen. 35:29
145. B. Gen. 49:30-31
146. D. Gen. 36:9
147. A. Gen. 36:9
148. B. Gen. 36:40
149. C. Gen. 37:5-8
150. D. Gen. 37:9
151. C. Gen. 37:26-27
152. D. Gen. 38:13-18, 27-30
153. B. Gen. 40:9-10
154. A. Gen. 40:12-14
155. C. Gen. 40:16-17
156. B. Gen. 40:18-19
157. A. Gen. 40:14-15, 23
158. D. Gen. 41:1-4
159. B. Gen. 41:5-7
160. A. Gen. 41:26 & 29
161. B. Gen. 41:27
162. D. Gen. 42:35
163. A. Gen. 42:37
164. C. Gen. 49:10
165. D. Gen. 50:13
166. B. Gen. 50:19-20
167. C. Exod. 1:15
168. A. Exod. 2:15
169. C. Exod. 2:16-18
170. A. Exod. 3:14
171. D. Exod. 4:2-3
172. C. Exod. 4:4
173. A. Exod. 4:6
174. C. Exod. 5:7
175. B. Exod. 6:3
176. D. Exod. 6:20
177. C. Exod. 8:18-19

178. A. Exod. 10:22
179. C. Exod. 12:13
180. C. Exod. 7:19; 8:2, 16,
     21; 9:3, 9, 18; 10:4,
     21; 11:5
181. A. Exod. 12:29
182. B. Exod. 13:2
183. C. Exod. 15:23-24
184. D. Exod. 15:25
185. A. Exod. 15:27
186. D. Exod. 16:35
187. C. Exod. 21:2
188. C. Exod. 23:10-11
189. D. Exod. 24:9
190. B. Exod. 24:13
191. B. Exod. 31:2-6
192. A. Exod. 32:26
193. C. Exod. 32:28
194. D. Exod. 34:28
195. B. Lev. 6:5
196. C. Lev. 8:23
197. A. Lev. 23:5
198. C. Lev. 23:6
199. D. Lev. 23:10-11
200. C. Lev. 23:15-16
201. B. Lev. 23:24
202. A. Lev. 23:27
203. B. Lev. 23:34
204. D. Lev. 24:10-11, 23
205. B. Lev. 25:11
206. A. Num. 5:19-21
207. D. Num. 6:1-8
208. C. Num. 6:13 & 18
209. B. Num. 8:15-18
210. C. Num. 8:24-25
211. A. Num. 11:1-3
212. D. Num. 11:16-17
213. C. Num. 11:26-28
214. B. Num. 14:40-45
215. D. Num. 15:32-36
216. D. Num. 16:1-2
217. A. Num. 16:17
218. C. Num. 16:35
219. B. Num. 16:39
220. D. Num. 16:49
221. B. Num. 17:8
222. A. Num. 20:14-18
223. A. Num. 20:27-28

224. D. Num. 20:29
225. C. Num. 21:1-3
226. B. Num. 21:21-24
227. C. Num. 21:33-35
228. B. Deut. 3:11
229. C. Deut. 3:11
230. D. Num. 25:1-2
231. C. Num. 25:6-8, 14-15
232. A. Num. 25:7
233. B. Num. 27:7
234. A. Num. 27:1
235. D. Num. 36:6
236. D. Num. 35:11
237. B. Num. 35:13
238. C. Num. 35:25
239. C. Deut. 1:3
240. D. Deut. 25:3
241. A. Deut. 25:17-19
242. C. Deut. 34:8
243. C. Josh. 1:1 & 5
244. C. Josh. 1:8
245. A. Josh. 1:12-15
246. B. Josh. 2:6
247. D. Josh. 2:6
248. B. Josh. 2:5
249. A. Josh. 5:13-14
250. D. Josh. 5:15
251. B. Josh. 6:26
252. B. Josh. 7:20-21
253. C. Josh. 7:22
254. C. Josh. 7:5
255. A. Josh. 7:24-25
256. D. Josh. 9:3-4, 21
257. C. Josh. 10:1
258. D. Josh. 10:16
259. D. Josh. 12:24
260. C. Josh. 14:6-7
261. D. Josh. 14:10
262. A. Josh. 14:13
263. B. Josh. 15:16-17
264. B. Josh. 18:1
265. D. Josh. 21:41
266. C. Josh. 22:10
267. A. Josh. 22:15-16
268. B. Josh. 22:34
269. D. Josh. 24:1
270. C. Judg. 1:6
271. B. Judg. 1:7

72

272. B. Judg. 1:19
273. B. Judg. 2:1-3
274. D. Judg. 1:12-13; 3:9-10
275. D. Judg. 3:12
276. A. Judg. 3:15-22
277. A. Judg. 4:2
278. D. Judg. 4:2
279. B. Judg. 4:4
280. C. Judg. 4:5-7
281. B. Judg. 4:6
282. A. Judg. 4:21-22
283. C. Judg. 5:1
284. D. Judg. 6:1
285. B. Judg. 6:11-12
286. B. Judg. 6:15
287. D. Judg. 6:25
288. A. Judg. 6:30-31
289. A. Judg. 6:30
290. B. Judg. 6:32
291. D. Judg. 7:2
292. B. Judg. 7:3
293. D. Judg. 7:5-7
294. C. Judg. 7:7
295. D. Judg. 7:10-11
296. C. Judg. 7:13
297. A. Judg. 7:13
298. B. Judg. 7:14
299. C. Judg. 7:16
300. A. Judg. 7:18
301. B. Judg. 7:25
302. D. Judg. 8:5-8
303. B. Judg. 8:5
304. C. Judg. 8:14-16
305. C. Judg. 8:17
306. A. Judg. 8:20
307. D. Judg. 8:30-31
308. A. Judg. 9:5
309. C. Judg. 9:6
310. D. Judg. 9:14
311. B. Judg. 9:28-29
312. B. Judg. 9:39 & 45
313. C. Judg. 9:53
314. A. Judg. 9:53-54
315. C. Judg. 16:3-4
316. B. Judg. 16:23
317. D. Judg. 16:30
318. B. Judg. 17:1-2
319. D. Judg. 17:9-10

320. A. Judg. 18:16-20
321. C. Judg. 19:15, 25-28
322. B. Judg. 19:14
323. B. Judg. 20:47
324. D. Judg. 21:12
325. C. Judg. 21:19-23
326. D. Ruth 1:4
327. A. Ruth 4:10
328. D. Ruth 1:3-5
329. B. Ruth 1:14-15
330. C. Ruth 1:16
331. C. Ruth 4:13-17
332. A. Ruth 4:17
333. D. Ruth 4:17
334. B. I Sam. 1:1-2
335. D. I Sam. 1:2
336. A. I Sam. 1:3
337. C. I Sam. 1:11
338. A. I Sam. 1:13
339. B. I Sam. 1:20
340. C. I Sam. 4:10-11
341. D. I Sam. 4:15-18
342. C. I Sam. 4:18
343. B. I Sam. 4:21
344. D. I Sam. 4:21
345. B. I Sam. 5:1
346. D. I Sam. 5:2
347. B. I Sam. 5:3
348. C. I Sam. 5:4
349. A. I Sam. 6:12-13
350. D. I Sam. 6:19
351. C. I Sam. 7:1-2
352. B. I Sam. 7:5-6
353. A. I Sam. 7:12
354. D. I Sam. 7:17
355. B. I Sam. 8:1-2
356. C. I Sam. 8:7
357. A. I Sam. 8:19-20
358. B. I Sam. 11:1-2
359. D. I Sam. 11:7 & 11
360. C. I Sam. 12:17-18
361. D. I Sam. 13:9-13
362. A. I Sam. 14:14
363. C. I Sam. 14:24
364. B. I Sam. 14:27
365. A. I Sam. 14:43-44
366. D. I Sam. 14:45
367. C. I Sam. 15:1-3

368. B. I Sam. 15:8
369. A. I Sam. 15:33
370. B. I Sam. 16:6-13
371. D. I Sam. 16:23
372. D. I Sam. 17:4
373. C. I Sam. 17:12
374. D. I Sam. 17:16
375. A. I Sam. 17:23
376. B. I Sam. 17:34-35
377. A. I Sam. 17:38-39
378. D. I Sam. 17:40
379. A. I Sam. 17:51
380. B. I Sam. 18:17
381. C. I Sam. 18:27
382. B. I Sam. 19:13-14
383. D. I Sam. 19:18
384. C. I Sam. 19:20-24
385. B. I Sam. 20:32-33
386. C. I Sam. 20:22
387. A. I Sam. 21:6
388. B. I Sam. 21:1
389. D. I Sam. 21:9
390. A. I Sam. 21:13
391. B. I Sam. 22:3-4
392. D. I Sam. 22:5
393. D. I Sam. 22:18
394. A. I Sam. 22:19
395. C. I Sam. 22:20-23
396. A. I Sam. 27:3
397. D. I Sam. 27:6
398. C. I Sam. 28:7-8
399. B. I Sam. 28:12
400. A. I Sam. 28:24-25
401. C. I Sam. 29:3-4
402. D. I Sam. 30:1
403. A. I Sam. 30:6
404. B. I Sam. 30:10
405. B. I Sam. 30:11
406. D. I Sam. 30:16
407. C. I Sam. 30:22
408. A. I Sam. 30:24
409. C. I Sam. 31:1
410. D. I Sam. 31:2
411. B. II Sam. 1:6-10
412. B. II Sam. 1:13-15
413. D. II Sam. 2:11
414. C. II Sam. 2:11
415. A. II Sam. 2:5

416. B. II Sam. 2:8-9
417. D. II Sam. 2:8
418. A. II Sam. 2:10
419. C. II Sam. 2:18
420. A. II Sam. 2:19-23
421. B. II Sam. 2:32
422. D. II Sam. 3:7-8
423. C. II Sam. 3:12
424. B. II Sam. 3:13
425. A. II Sam. 3:27
426. A. II Sam. 3:32
427. D. II Sam. 4:4
428. B. II Sam. 4:4
429. C. II Sam. 4:4-6
430. B. II Sam. 4:8
431. B. II Sam. 4:12
432. A. II Sam. 4:12
433. C. I Chron. 11:4
434. A. I Chron. 11:6
435. C. II Sam. 5:5
436. A. II Sam. 5:24
437. D. II Sam. 6:3
438. B. II Sam. 6:6-7
439. C. II Sam. 6:10
440. B. II Sam. 6:11
441. A. II Sam. 7:12-13
442. C. II Sam. 9:2
443. D. II Sam. 9:6-7
444. C. II Sam. 9:10
445. B. II Sam. 9:9-10
446. A. II Sam. 10:1-2
447. D. II Sam. 10:4
448. D. II Sam. 10:6
449. B. II Sam. 10:10
450. C. II Sam. 11:14-15
451. A. II Sam. 11:3, 26-27
452. B. II Sam. 12:4
453. B. II Sam. 12:5
454. D. II Sam. 12:7
455. C. II Sam. 12:13-14
456. D. II Sam. 12:24
457. B. II Sam. 13:1
458. C. II Sam. 13:10-14
459. A. II Sam. 13:28-29
460. A. II Sam. 14:1-3
461. C. II Sam. 14:21
462. D. II Sam. 14:23
463. B. II Sam. 14:24

464. C. II Sam. 14:29-30
465. D. II Sam. 14:33
466. B. II Sam. 15:29
467. A. II Sam. 15:29
468. C. II Sam. 16:3
469. D. II Sam. 16:9
470. B. II Sam. 17:1-2
471. A. II Sam. 17:23
472. C. II Sam. 17:15-17
473. D. II Sam. 17:18
474. B. II Sam. 17:25
475. D. II Sam. 17:25
476. C. II Sam. 18:2
477. B. II Sam. 18:9
478. B. II Sam. 18:19
479. A. II Sam. 18:21
480. A. II Sam. 18:23
481. D. II Sam. 19:5-8
482. C. II Sam. 19:13
483. D. II Sam. 19:21
484. C. II Sam. 19:25-27
485. B. II Sam. 21:1
486. D. II Sam. 21:6
487. C. II Sam. 21:9
488. D. II Sam. 21:10
489. A. II Sam. 21:14
490. B. II Sam. 21:16-17
491. C. II Sam. 23:1
492. B. II Sam. 23:16
493. D. II Sam. 23:16
494. A. I Kings 1:7
495. C. I Kings 1:7
496. D. I Kings 1:33
497. B. I Kings 1:39
498. B. I Kings 3:5
499. A. I Kings 7:13-14
500. C. I Kings 7:21
501. D. I Kings 9:11-12
502. B. I Kings 10:1-3
503. A. I Kings 10:18
504. D. I Kings 11:3
505. C. I Kings 11:3
506. D. I Kings 11:30-31
507. B. I Kings 11:30-31
508. A. I Kings 11:30
509. C. I Kings 11:40
510. C. I Kings 11:42
511. D. I Kings 12:6-7

512. B. I Kings 12:8-11
513. B. I Kings 12:13-14
514. A. I Kings 12:18
515. D. I Kings 12:22-24
516. C. I Kings 12:26-29
517. D. I Kings 13:1-2
518. A. I Kings 13:4
519. B. I Kings 13:5
520. C. I Kings 13:6
521. C. I Kings 13:20-22
522. D. I Kings 13:24
523. A. I Kings 14:1
524. C. I Kings 14:2
525. D. I Kings 14:12
526. B. I Kings 14:25
527. B. I Kings 14:27
528. C. I Kings 15:13
529. B. II Chron. 15:1 & 2
530. A. I Kings 15:18
531. D. II Chron. 16:7
532. D. II Chron. 16:10
533. B. II Chron. 16:12
534. B. I Kings 16:28
535. C. I Kings 18:7
536. A. I Kings 18:4
537. D. I Kings 18:31-32
538. D. I Kings 18:33-34
539. B. I Kings 20:1-2
540. C. I Kings 20:13
541. A. I Kings 20:22
542. B. I Kings 20:29
543. A. I Kings 20:35
544. C. I Kings 20:36
545. D. I Kings 20:32-34, 42
546. B. I Kings 21:1-2
547. A. I Kings 21:13
548. D. I Kings 21:13
549. B. I Kings 21:17-18
550. C. I Kings 22:3-4
551. D. I Kings 22:26-27
552. A. I Kings 22:30
553. A. II Chron. 19:2
554. C. I Kings 22:37
555. C. II Kings 1:2
556. A. II Kings 1:2
557. A. II Kings 1:3-4
558. C. II Kings 1:9-10
559. C. II Kings 1:11-12

560. A. II Kings 1:13-15
561. B. II Kings 2:17
562. B. II Kings 3:4
563. A. II Kings 3:6-7
564. C. II Kings 3:9
565. D. II Kings 3:11
566. A. II Kings 3:15
567. D. II Kings 3:16
568. B. II Kings 3:22-24
569. C. II Kings 3:26-27
570. D. II Kings 4:16
571. A. II Kings 4:18-20
572. B. II Kings 4:31
573. D. II Kings 4:35
574. D. II Kings 6:12
575. C. II Kings 6:17
576. C. II Kings 6:18
577. A. II Kings 6:19
578. A. II Kings 6:23
579. B. II Kings 6:31
580. B. II Kings 7:1-2
581. C. II Kings 7:3-5
582. D. II Kings 7:17
583. B. II Kings 9:1-3
584. A. II Kings 9:22-24
585. C. II Kings 9:25
586. D. II Kings 9:27
587. A. II Kings 9:30-33
588. C. II Kings 10:17
589. D. II Kings 10:23-24
590. C. II Kings 10:30
591. A. II Kings 11:1-2
592. B. II Kings 11:21
593. C. II Kings 12:2
594. D. II Kings 12:9
595. C. II Kings 12:18
596. B. II Chron. 24:20
597. C. II Chron. 24:20
598. C. II Chron. 24:21
599. B. II Kings 13:14
600. C. II Kings 13:18
601. B. II Kings 13:18
602. A. II Kings 13:19
603. A. II Chron. 26:1
604. C. II Chron. 26:19
605. C. II Kings 17:23
606. A. II Kings 17:25
607. C. II Kings 19:14

608. C. II Kings 22:14
609. A. II Kings 23:21
610. B. II Kings 23:29
611. D. II Kings 25:8
612. A. Ezra 4:7
613. D. Ezra 4:21
614. B. Ezra 5:6
615. C. Ezra 6:7
616. D. Neh. 4:3
617. A. Neh. 5:7
618. D. Neh. 7:2
619. B. Neh. 8:2-3
620. D. Neh. 8:10
621. B. Neh. 13:8
622. A. Job 1:1
623. B. Job 1:2
624. D. Job 1:3
625. C. Job 1:3
626. A. Job 1:3
627. B. Job 1:3
628. A. Job 2:11
629. D. Job 2:11
630. C. Job 2:11
631. C. Job 4:1; 15:1; 22:1
632. C. Job 8:1; 18:1; 25:1
633. B. Job 11:1; 20:1
634. D. Job 32:2
635. A. Job 13:15
636. B. Job 19:25
637. C. Job 42:14
638. D. Ps. 19:1
639. B. Ps. 23:1
640. B. Ps. 90
641. D. Ps. 117
642. C. Ps. 119
643. D. Ps. 119:176
644. A. Prov. 14:12
645. C. Prov. 18:24
646. B. Prov. 20:29
647. D. Prov. 29:18
648. D. Prov. 31:10
649. B. Eccles. 1:1
650. C. Song of Sol. 1:1
651. C. Isa. 1:1
652. A. Isa. 1:18
653. D. Isa. 26:3
654. B. Isa. 44:28
655. C. Isa. 53:4-9

656. D. Jer. 1:1
657. B. Jer. 1:1
658. A. Jer. 13:4
659. B. Jer. 15:1
660. C. Jer. 20:2
661. A. Jer. 20:6
662. D. Jer. 24:1
663. B. Jer. 26:18
664. C. Jer. 26:20-23
665. A. Jer. 28:1-4
666. C. Jer. 28:10
667. D. Jer. 28:16-17
668. B. Jer. 32:9
669. D. Jer. 35:5-6
670. A. Jer. 36:28
671. B. Jer. 38:6
672. D. Jer. 38:12-13
673. C. Jer. 38:12
674. D. Jer. 41:2
675. C. Ezek. 1:6
676. C. Ezek. 3:17
677. A. Ezek. 23:4
678. B. Ezek. 23:4
679. C. Ezek. 23:4
680. A. Ezek. 24:18
681. D. Dan. 1:7
682. A. Dan. 1:7
683. B. Dan. 1:7
684. C. Dan. 1:7
685. C. Dan. 1:15
686. D. Dan. 2:12
687. A. Dan. 4:1, 10, 14
688. A. Dan. 4:19-22
689. B. Dan. 5:27-30
690. C. Dan. 7:4
691. A. Dan. 7:5
692. D. Dan. 7:6
693. B. Dan. 7:7
694. A. Dan. 7:8
695. C. Dan. 8:20
696. D. Dan. 8:21
697. B. Dan. 8:16
698. A. Dan. 9:2
699. B. Hos. 1:3-4
700. D. Hos. 1:6
701. B. Hos. 1:8-9
702. D. Amos 7:10
703. B. Jonah 4:6

704. D. Jonah 4:7
705. C. Mic. 6:8
706. A. Zech. 3:1-3
707. B. Zech. 4:6
708. C. Zech. 11:7
709. D. Mal. 4:5
710. B. Matt. 1:17
711. A. Matt. 2:16
712. C. Matt. 2:15
713. D. Matt. 2:22
714. B. Matt. 3:4
715. B. Matt. 3:6
716. A. Matt. 3:13-14
717. C. Matt. 6:20
718. D. Matt. 7:29
719. B. Matt. 8:2
720. C. Matt. 8:8-10
721. A. Matt. 8:19-20
722. B. Matt. 8:31-32
723. A. Matt. 8:34
724. C. Matt. 9:14
725. D. Matt. 9:37
726. C. Matt. 10:16
727. B. Matt. 11:12-14
728. A. Matt. 11:23-24
729. C. Matt. 12:31
730. C. Matt. 13:4
731. B. Matt. 13:5
732. D. Matt. 13:7
733. A. Matt. 13:8
734. C. Matt. 13:25
735. D. Matt. 13:39
736. A. Matt. 13:37
737. C. Matt. 13:39
738. C. Matt. 13:31-32
739. B. Matt. 15:26
740. D. Matt. 16:23
741. A. Matt. 16:26
742. B. Matt. 17:9
743. C. Matt. 17:20
744. D. Matt. 17:20
745. B. Matt. 17:24-27
746. C. Matt. 18:21
747. B. Matt. 18:24
748. C. Matt. 18:28
749. B. Matt. 20:28
750. D. Matt. 20:29-30
751. A. Matt. 21:9

752. A. Matt. 21:17
753. C. Matt. 22:16-17
754. D. Matt. 22:23
755. D. Matt. 22:25-26
756. B. Matt. 22:41-42
757. A. Matt. 23:11
758. D. Matt. 23:13
759. D. Matt. 23:24
760. A. Matt. 23:27
761. C. Matt. 25:1
762. B. Matt. 25:2
763. D. Matt. 25:6
764. C. Matt. 25:15
765. B. Matt. 25:15
766. A. Matt. 25:15
767. D. Matt. 25:16
768. C. Matt. 25:17
769. A. Matt. 25:18
770. B. Matt. 25:28
771. D. Matt. 25:33
772. C. Matt. 26:53
773. B. Matt. 26:74-75
774. A. Matt. 27:46-47
775. C. Matt. 27:52-53
776. D. Matt. 27:59-60
777. A. Matt. 28:2
778. B. Matt. 28:16
779. D. Mark 2:3
780. C. Mark 2:4
781. C. Mark 2:5
782. B. Mark 4:1
783. A. Mark 5:2, 9
784. D. Mark 5:22, 39
785. C. Mark 6:14
786. B. Mark 6:25
787. D. Mark 7:21
788. C. Mark 7:34
789. D. Mark 8:22-25
790. B. Mark 10:35-37
791. B. Mark 12:42
792. D. Mark 12:42
793. D. Mark 13:14
794. A. Luke 1:3
795. C. Luke 1:32
796. B. Luke 1:39-40
797. A. Luke 1:59
798. D. Luke 2:41-42
799. B. Luke 2:46

800. C. Luke 3:1
801. B. Luke 3:8
802. A. Luke 3:14
803. D. Luke 3:38
804. B. Luke 4:1
805. A. Luke 4:16 & 29
806. D. Luke 7:33
807. B. Luke 9:54
808. A. Luke 13:1
809. C. Luke 13:4
810. C. Luke 13:11
811. D. Luke 14:28
812. B. Luke 16:13
813. D. Luke 18:13
814. B. Luke 22:43
815. A. Luke 24:18
816. B. John 1:44
817. A. John 1:48
818. C. John 2:8-9
819. A. John 2:19
820. B. John 2:20
821. C. John 3:1
822. B. John 4:5-6
823. D. John 4:10
824. C. John 4:24
825. D. John 5:46
826. A. John 12:10-11
827. B. John 13:2
828. D. John 13:3-5
829. C. John 13:34
830. B. John 15:5
831. A. John 18:28
832. D. John 19:22
833. B. John 20:11, 14-15
834. C. John 21:11
835. A. Acts 1:23
836. C. Acts 2:17
837. C. Acts 3:1
838. D. Acts 4:36
839. B. Acts 5:1
840. A. Acts 5:15
841. C. Acts 5:34-37
842. D. Acts 6:11
843. C. Acts 7:58
844. D. Acts 8:9 & 13
845. B. Acts 8:18-20
846. A. Acts 11:22
847. B. Acts 11:25-26

848. D. Acts 11:28
849. C. Acts 11:28
850. B. Acts 11:29-30
851. A. Acts 12:25
852. D. Acts 13:6
853. B. Acts 13:8
854. C. Acts 13:9-11
855. C. Acts 15:27
856. D. Acts 16:14
857. B. Acts 16:16-18
858. C. Acts 16:26
859. A. Acts 16:27
860. D. Acts 16:37-38
861. B. Acts 17:23
862. D. Acts 18:2
863. C. Acts 18:2
864. B. Acts 18:12
865. D. Acts 18:17
866. B. Acts 18:18
867. A. Acts 18:24
868. C. Acts 18:26
869. D. Acts 19:6-7
870. B. Acts 19:9
871. A. Acts 19:11-12
872. C. Acts 19:13-14
873. D. Acts 19:33-34
874. C. Acts 19:35
875. B. Acts 20:16
876. D. Acts 21:10-11
877. B. Acts 21:26-27
878. A. Acts 21:31-33
879. C. Acts 23:26
880. A. Acts 22:2
881. D. Acts 23:2
882. B. Acts 23:7
883. C. Acts 24:1
884. A. Acts 27:1
885. B. Acts 27:37
886. C. Acts 28:3-4
887. B. Acts 28:6
888. A. Acts 28:7
889. D. Acts 28:8
890. B. Acts 28:11
891. B. Acts 28:30
892. D. Rom. 1:1,16
893. C. Rom. 4:1
894. A. Rom. 3:23
895. C. Rom. 6:23

896. B. Rom. 16:22
897. D. I Cor. 13:1
898. B. I Cor. 15:12
899. A. I Cor. 15:22
900. C. II Cor. 9:7
901. A. Gal. 2:11
902. D. Gal. 4:6
903. B. Phil. 4:2
904. D. Phil. 4:18
905. C. Col. 4:12
906. B. Col. 4:16
907. C. Col. 4:14
908. D. I Tim. 1:3
909. A. 2 Tim. 3:8
910. D. Titus 1:5
911. D. Philem. 10, 16
912. B. Philem. 10
913. C. Heb. 5:5-6
914. D. Heb. 11:4
915. B. Heb. 11:5
916. A. Heb. 12:2
917. C. James 1:3
918. A. James 1:22
919. D. James 2:26
920. B. James 3:8
921. C. James 4:7
922. D. James 5:11
923. B. I Peter 5:8
924. A. 2 Peter 3:15
925. B. 3 John 1
926. D. 3 John 9
927. C. Jude 1
928. C. Rev. 1:4
929. B. Rev. 1:20
930. A. Rev. 2:1 & 4
931. B. Rev. 2:18-20
932. D. Rev. 3:14-16
933. C. Rev. 4:4
934. B. Rev. 4:5
935. A. Rev. 4:8
936. C. Rev. 4:8
937. C. Rev. 5:1
938. D. Rev. 6:1-2
939. A. Rev. 6:3-4
940. C. Rev. 6:5
941. B. Rev. 6:5
942. D. Rev. 6:7-8
943. D. Rev. 6:8

944. A. Rev. 6:8
945. C. Rev. 6:9
946. D. Rev. 6:12-13
947. C. Rev. 7:4
948. D. Rev. 7:5-8
949. A. Rev. 8:1
950. B. Rev. 8:7
951. D. Rev. 8:8
952. C. Rev. 8:10-11
953. D. Rev. 8:12
954. A. Rev. 9:1-3
955. D. Rev. 9:11
956. B. Rev. 9:11
957. C. Rev. 9:13-14
958. D. Rev. 9:16
959. C. Rev. 10:3-4
960. A. Rev. 10:8-10
961. D. Rev. 11:1-2
962. B. Rev. 11:3
963. A. Rev. 11:4
964. D. Rev. 11:7
965. C. Rev. 11:8
966. C. Rev. 11:11
967. B. Rev. 11:13
968. A. Rev. 11:15
969. C. Rev. 12:1
970. D. Rev. 12:7
971. D. Rev. 12:9
972. A. Rev. 13:2
973. B. Rev. 13:2
974. D. Rev. 13:5
975. A. Rev. 13:11
976. C. Rev. 13:11-14
977. D. Rev. 13:15
978. A. Rev. 13:17
979. C. Rev. 13:18
980. B. Rev. 15:7
981. A. Rev. 16:2
982. C. Rev. 16:3
983. D. Rev. 16:4
984. C. Rev. 16:8-9
985. A. Rev. 16:10
986. B. Rev. 16:12
987. A. Rev. 16:12
988. B. Rev. 16:17-18
989. C. Rev. 16:21
990. D. Rev. 18:10-11
991. A. Rev. 19:11-13

992. D. Rev. 20:1-2
993. B. Rev. 21:2
994. D. Rev. 21:12
995. A. Rev. 21:12

996. C. Rev. 21:12
997. B. Rev. 21:21
998. D. Rev. 21:14

999. B. Rev. 21:14
1000. A. Rev. 21:21
1001. D. Rev. 22:2